Saving Energy *and* $ at Home

What to Have Done... *and Why*

Larry   Tim   Tom

Tim Snyder, Tom Casey & Larry Janesky

Saving Energy _and $_ at Home

What to Have Done... _and Why_

by Tim Snyder, Tom Casey and Larry Janesky

Graphic Design & Editing by Katherine Ceddia

Editorial Advisor: Larry Walters

Published by:

Dr. Energy Saver Holding, LLC

28 Progress Ave., Seymour, CT 06483

1-877-4RX-ENERGY

1-877-(479-3637)

www.DrEnergySaver.com

ISBN 978-0-9776457-6-3

This book is dedicated to the fine, hard-working people at Dr. Energy Saver™ Franchises across North America who help people conserve energy, save money, and contribute to a better environment.

www.DrEnergySaver.com

Table of Contents

How to Use this Book
A Reader's Guide

There are 11 brief chapters, each dealing with a specific aspect of saving energy at home. There are photographs and sidebars in each chapter to help you understand the idea. In addition, there are 8 different symbols that have different meanings:

Important

This is important!

Apples & Oranges

The two products or systems discussed are very different.

Side Note

Additional Information

This is a BIG IDEA!

This subject is very important in getting the results you want.

You'll Love This!

You will love the results from this!

CAUTION

Beware, don't make this mistake.

MOLD

This is especially important to prevent mold.

Important for the resale value of your home.

INTRODUCTION

Your Prescription for Lower Energy Bills™

It's Time To Start Saving Energy!

Energy is easy to take for granted

Another day begins. *The coffee is brewing, and you've just turned up the thermostat to get the house nice and warm. You flip on the bathroom light and step into a nice hot shower.*

All of these everyday activities, along with countless others, require energy. Energy offers us warmth, comfort, convenience, security and even luxury. It enables us not only to survive, but to learn, grow, and thrive. And yet, we often take energy for granted. We don't think about the trainloads of coal traveling across the country to reach generating stations. We don't see the huge tanker offloading a million barrels of crude oil after traveling halfway around the world. And we aren't aware of the maintenance crews checking miles of natural gas pipeline so we can enjoy a hot breakfast.

If you're concerned about how your house uses energy, loses energy and wastes money, *this book is for you*.

But our energy awareness has increased lately. For one thing, we're paying a lot more for all of the energy we consume. And in addition to a higher dollar cost, burning fossil fuels has an environmental cost we can't ignore. Today there's a double incentive to make our homes more energy efficient. It's personal and it's also global.

Take the ✓ QUIZ

☐ I want to save energy.

☐ I want to save money.

☐ I want to do something positive for the environment.

Don't check one; check all three. The truth is that if you're saving energy, you're also saving money and helping to preserve our environment. As many experts have pointed out, saving energy can and should be a global initiative. If we all pitch in, we'll have a better planet we can pass on to future generations.

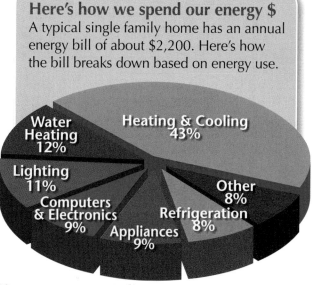

Here's how we spend our energy $
A typical single family home has an annual energy bill of about $2,200. Here's how the bill breaks down based on energy use.

Heating & Cooling 43%
Water Heating 12%
Lighting 11%
Computers & Electronics 9%
Appliances 9%
Refrigeration 8%
Other 8%

(The heating or cooling numbers will change based on how far north or south you are.)

Mr. and Mrs. Leakey loved their historic house. They enjoyed showing off all the well-preserved moldings and the beautiful oak floor. But as winter approached, they dreaded having the same argument about covering the floor with carpeting. "You know I can't stand how cold the floor gets," began Mrs. Leakey.

"Don't worry," replied Mr. Leakey reassuringly. "I went down in the crawl space and wedged some foam insulation board between the joists," he explained. Mr. Leakey shuddered when he remembered working in the dark, damp space, but was proud of himself for tackling the project. "It's going to be OK this winter, you'll see," he said.

But it wasn't. After several days of cold weather, it was clear that cold drafts were still coming in around the floor's heat registers. The floor wasn't warmer either." Are you sure you installed that insulation the right way?" Mrs. Leakey asked. Dismayed, Mr. Leakey returned to the crawl space, this time with a more powerful light. The insulation he installed was still in place, but the light revealed gaps in the insulation, and there were areas he wasn't able to reach.

"How am I going to get insulation back there?" he wondered. Then he noticed mold growing on the floor joists. Even though he hated being down in the crawl space, he was dreading the trip back upstairs.

Not if we run out, *but when...*

To power our vehicles and generate the electricity that powers everything else, we rely primarily on oil (petroleum), natural gas, coal and uranium. These are all **non-renewable energy sources**. When these natural resources were first discovered, nobody worried about depleting the vast reserves that existed around the world. Today we have a better appreciation for what "non-renewable" means: Sooner or later, we run out. That's why it's important to save energy. As you'll see in Chapter 11, we're getting better about developing **renewable energy sources**. But we're still going to be using oil and gas for a long time, so it makes sense to use it as wisely and economically as possible.

Alaska Pipeline

The Pipeline Can't Run Forever. *About 20% of U.S. domestic oil production makes the 800-mile trip through the Alaska Pipeline. While we can't eliminate our need for oil, we can become less dependent on foreign oil by making our homes more energy efficient.*

Marilyn Hotts hadn't spent a moment missing the cold weather since moving south last winter. But she was worried about her electric bill, which had been steadily increasing with the onset of summer. She had an HVAC contractor service her air conditioning system, but that didn't seem to make a dent in the heat she felt in her upstairs bedroom. "I've still got a problem upstairs," she explained when calling the contractor back "I have the downstairs thermostat set to 65. I need to wear a sweater in my kitchen. But upstairs my bedroom's still too hot and I can't sleep at night."

"There's nothing wrong with your AC unit," the contractor replied. "I'm not sure there's anything else I can do."

Marilyn unpacked a few more sweaters to cope with the cold in her kitchen. But she still was tossing and turning at night because of the heat in her bedroom. Then her next electric bill arrived, forcing her to call her utility company.

"I didn't count on paying this much for electricity every month!" she said.

"In a few months, it'll start getting cool again," the operator offered. "A lot of folks have trouble adjusting when they first move down here. You'll get used to it."

Marilyn continued to worry. "I have to get a good night's sleep! Who can I call now?"

FOSSIL FUELS: millions of years to make, *just a few moments to burn*

It takes millions of years for the earth to produce coal, oil, and natural gas – the non-renewable fossil fuels we use to generate power and heat. Today we are burning through these non-renewable resources at an ever-increasing pace. The need to reduce our consumption and waste of fossil fuels will only become greater in the future. Here's why:

- **Fossil fuel costs will continue to rise.** Increased global demand for oil, coal and natural gas drives prices up. Production costs also continue to rise, because the most accessible deposits of these resources have been used up.

- **Self-sufficiency = security.** The United States uses more fuel per capita than any country in the world, and we import over 50% of our fuel. It's risky to put other countries in charge of our fuel supply. By using less fuel overall, and more fuel from our own reserves, we can improve our national security.

- **Burning fossil fuels is bad for the environment.** The carbon that's released into the atmosphere when we burn oil, coal, and natural gas contributes to air pollution and global warming.

Cutting household <u>electric</u> bills can cut down on air pollution. Most of our electricity comes from coal-fired power plants located throughout the country. The carbon emissions from burning coal and other fossil fuels to generate your household electricity contributes to air pollution and global warming.

The Greens were very interested in sustainable living and environmental issues. When they heard about an energy-saving program that was available through their local utility, they jumped at the chance. "We've already got a hybrid car," Mrs. Green said. "Making our house more energy-efficient will reduce our carbon footprint even more," she continued.

The two technicians from the utility company put weatherstripping on the Green's front door, replaced 14 lightbulbs with compact fluorescent bulbs and installed a new furnace filter. They also left the Greens with a list of things they could do to save energy, like upgrading their appliances and using low-flow showerheads.

"We're doing a lot of this stuff already," Mr. Green replied after reading down the list. "I'm disappointed. Except for the weatherstripping on the door, we haven't done anything to reduce the energy we use for heating and cooling."

Mrs. Green sighed. "Isn't there something else we can do?"

Why should I save energy at my home?

This is a good question. This is Larry Janesky writing here. We are all free to do what we want, and most of us don't want to be forced to do anything, and we don't want to do it out of fear. I can tell you that I am not an alarmist going around telling everyone the sky is falling. And you may have thought that we'd take that approach in this book, especially when the name of your company is "Dr. Energy Saver". But we aren't.

This **is a BIG IDEA!**

While I am not an alarmist, I am a realist. As of this writing, it is October 2009. Things will likely change quickly. Consider all these facts.

World oil demand is going up. Indeed, there are 2000 more cars registered in Shanghai each WEEK, and 2009 car sales in India rose 25% over 2008, despite the global recession. (And don't blame them, the US still uses the most oil by FAR).

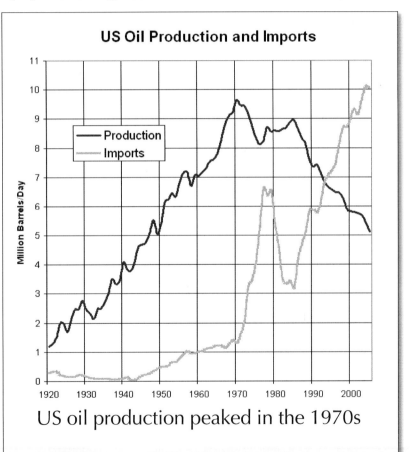

US Oil Production and Imports

— Production
····· Imports

Million Barrels/Day

US oil production peaked in the 1970s

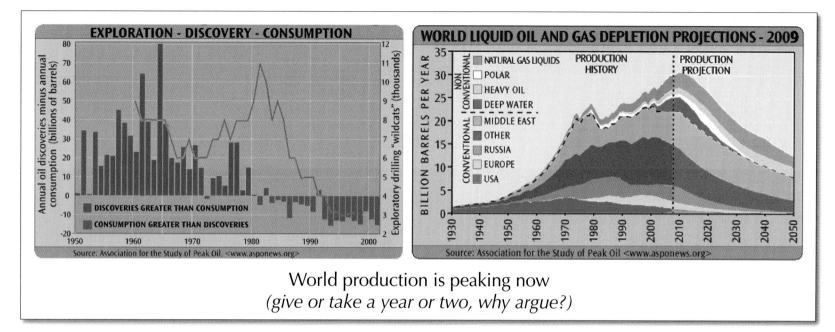

EXPLORATION - DISCOVERY - CONSUMPTION

Annual oil discoveries minus annual consumption (billions of barrels)

Exploratory drilling "wildcats" (thousands)

DISCOVERIES GREATER THAN CONSUMPTION
CONSUMPTION GREATER THAN DISCOVERIES

Source: Association for the Study of Peak Oil, <www.asponews.org>

WORLD LIQUID OIL AND GAS DEPLETION PROJECTIONS - 2009

BILLION BARRELS PER YEAR

NON CONVENTIONAL / CONVENTIONAL

- NATURAL GAS LIQUIDS
- POLAR
- HEAVY OIL
- DEEP WATER
- MIDDLE EAST
- OTHER
- RUSSIA
- EUROPE
- USA

PRODUCTION HISTORY

PRODUCTION PROJECTION

Source: Association for the Study of Peak Oil <www.asponews.org>

World production is peaking now
(give or take a year or two, why argue?)

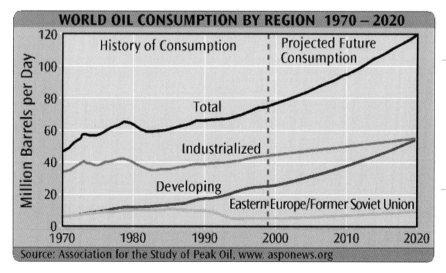

WORLD OIL CONSUMPTION BY REGION 1970 – 2020

Million Barrels per Day

History of Consumption | Projected Future Consumption

Total

Industrialized

Developing

Eastern Europe/Former Soviet Union

Source: Association for the Study of Peak Oil, www. asponews.org

Here's a quote for us – *"All the easy oil and gas in the world has pretty much been found. Now comes the harder work in finding and producing oil from more challenging environments and work areas."*

-William J. Cummings, Exxon-Mobil company spokesman, December 2005

www.DrEnergySaver.com

World population is growing

– every 110 hours we add 1 million people! And we add a billion people every 14 years or so.

Sure, technology will help get more oil out of oilfields, but this oil is more expensive.

What drives prices? – the same thing that always has – supply and demand. The world supply curve will very shortly cross below the world demand curve. When this happens, prices will begin to skyrocket, this time, never to return to the "Good old days".

So why should you save energy at home? For most, we're going to HAVE TO in the near future, because they simply can't afford to heat, cool, and buy electricity.

"It is better to do a thing before you <u>have</u> to."
— Larry Janesky

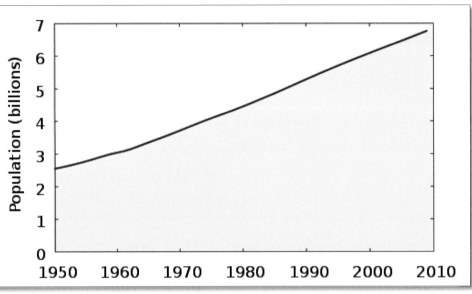

Let's say you save $700 a year in energy at today's prices. When prices double, this number is $1,400 a year. When prices quadruple, you'll save $2,800 a year, and probably be clamoring to save more, along with many millions of others at the same time (which will make repairs more costly then).

When will that be? I don't know. **You guess.**

Why aren't energy prices very high in 2009?

The Energy Information Administration said in their report on July 11, 2007 *"It looks like we're going to need a good recession to avoid much higher energy prices over the next few years."* ...and that's just what we got.

One thing we cannot deny - oil is being used up, and we are highly dependent on it. Once demand passes supply, the price will race ahead. And, the more abruptly we "run out" of oil, the more chaos it will cause. Think about it. How will we drive a car, fly airplanes, heat our homes and buildings, manufacture goods, or generate electricity with very high priced oil and gas – or eventually, with none at all. I will be leaving my three children a very different place than we have had – and you will too, that's for sure.

"Our ignorance is not so vast as our failure to use what we know."

-M. King Hubbert, who, in the 1950s, accurately predicted peak oil production in the US and the world.

There is lot more at stake for all of us than most of us realize today, but soon will. For these reasons, saving energy is something that this practical realist believes in very much. I don't believe in it because I am in the business, I am in the business because I believe in it.

Step one is to make our homes (and other places we use energy), as efficient as possible. (I have done much to my home and lowered my electric and gas bills by 40% (without "rebuilding" my house! It works!) Dr. Energy Saver can get this done for you.

The second step, to be done ONLY after the first, is to switch to alternate sources of energy before we HAVE to. (We have one of the largest solar installations in the state on our building, and I have a 10 kilowatt solar array on my home).

I want to be careful not to be an alarmist. We are all free to believe and do what we wish, as we should be. Yet only tomorrow, history will tell the tale. – Larry Janesky

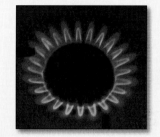
"Human history becomes more and more a race between education and catastrophe."

-H. G. Wells

Energy = heat, and heat moves in 3 ways

When it's cold outside, heat energy keeps our living spaces warm. Whether you're using it or losing it, heat energy moves in 3 different ways. Radiant heat can travel through space and warm objects that absorb it. The sun, a fire and an electric baseboard heater all rely on radiation to move heat. Heat can move by conduction, passing from a warmer object to a cooler object when both objects are touching each other. Finally, heat also moves through your house by convection. Since warm air is lighter than cool air, it rises to the upper areas of your house (where it leaks out). Outdoors, air sinks when it cools down, allowing the cycle to repeat.

Radiation: **Conduction:** **Convection:**

"Hey, Duke, doesn't that fire feel good?"

"Ouch! That poker's too hot to hold with my bare hands."

"I'll turn on the fan. All the warmest air is up near the ceiling."

The Pennypinchers prided themselves on their ability to save money on just about anything. They clipped coupons, shopped at discount stores, and made restaurants a once-a-month treat. Scrimping on nearly everything had enabled the family to move into a beautiful house and send two kids to college. But the upcoming winter had the parents worried.

"I don't know how we're going to pay to heat the house if fuel gets expensive this winter," Mr. Pennypincher confessed. "I know it's awfully uncomfortable, but we're going to have to keep the thermostat down even lower than it was last winter," he warned.

"C'mon Dad, last winter we all wore long underwear indoors," complained the youngest daughter. "I'm embarrassed to have friends over, and one of these days I'm afraid I'll be able to see my breath when I wake up in the morning."

Mrs. Pennypincher replied, "You know fuel is very expensive, I don't know what else we can do."

"I want to improve my home's energy-efficiency. How much can I expect to save?"

It all depends on the energy-saving upgrades you choose to make. Your home energy budget contains a number of categories, including heating and cooling, water heating, lighting, and appliances. It makes sense to focus on the largest cost areas, because they offer the greatest savings potential. For example, by focusing on upgrades that affect heating and cooling costs (air-sealing, insulation, ductwork and HVAC performance), you could cut heating/cooling expenses by up to 40% or more - and that's some real money!

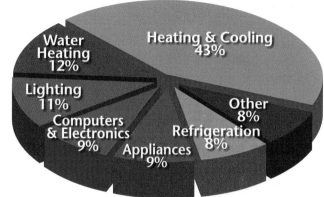

Heating & Cooling 43%
Water Heating 12%
Lighting 11%
Computers & Electronics 9%
Appliances 9%
Refrigeration 8%
Other 8%

"How do I get started?"

Contact Dr. Energy Saver at *www.DrEnergySaver.com* and schedule your Energy Saving Checkup™. Once Dr. Energy Saver arrives at your house, it will just take a couple of hours for you to have a complete home energy diagnosis that covers 10 areas of potential energy savings:

1. Air sealing

2. Insulation

3. Radiant Barriers

4. Ductwork

5. Heating & Air Conditioning

6. Water Heating

7. Lighting

8. Water Conservation

9. Windows & Doors

10. Appliances & Home Electronics

Lowering your home's energy usage is a smart investment that will start saving you money right away. Plus, it will improve your home's resale value. Your Dr. Energy Saver report will not only grade all 10 areas of energy performance with a "Home Energy Report Card"; it will tell you which upgrades should be done first.

Thinking BEYOND THE BOX: a WHOLE-HOUSE approach to energy savings

Wouldn't it be great if you could buy a single improvement, "energy saving in a box," that would solve your home energy problems? Saving energy would be a lot simpler if you could "just" add more insulation, or "just" replace your old water heater, or "just" upgrade to new energy-efficient windows, or "just" change your light bulbs.

The truth is that each of these "boxes" could definitely result in improved energy performance and reduced utility costs. But your home's energy equation involves many variables. It's not possible to cure your home's energy ills by checking off a single box. If a contractor or salesman insists that paying for a single repair or upgrade will solve your home energy problems, you can be sure you're being taken for a ride on the 'Optimism Express'. That's why it's wise to step away from the vehicle and give Dr. Energy Saver a call.

Many systems *interact* to determine how efficiently your house uses energy

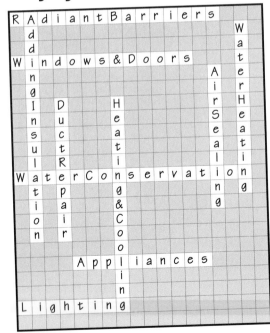

Your house is made up of many systems that serve your needs – for lighting, hot and cold water, comfortable indoor temperatures, healthy air quality, and power for appliances and plenty of other electrical devices. These systems interact, which means that when one system isn't working like it should, it affects the way other systems work. For example:

- Leaks in your duct system make your heating and cooling systems work harder, wasting energy and costing you money.

- The money you pay for hot water depends not only on the condition of your water heater, but also on pipe insulation, the faucets and showerheads in your house, and the efficiency of your dishwasher and washing machine.

- To save money on your electric bill, you have to consider improvements in many systems –lighting, appliances, air conditioning, heating, and water use, just for starters. Indirectly, air-sealing, insulation, ductwork, and even radiant barriers determine how much you pay for electricity every month.

*Dr. Energy Saver makes it **simple** for you.*

Dr. Energy Saver's WHOLE-HOUSE APPROACH
gives every system in your house the attention it deserves

Save Energy
Save Money
Save the Environment

If you're serious about saving energy, saving money, and helping to save the environment, don't take a chance on singular solutions. You and your house deserve the total picture. By evaluating all the systems in your house – the 10 Energy Vital Signs – Dr. Energy Saver makes sure that you get the most from your investment in energy savings. You'll avoid making improvements in one system that will be nullified because you ignored another.

Instead of calling 7 or 8 specialists, just call *one*

Making all the improvements identified in a home energy checkup would be a nightmare if you had to call individual contractors to perform all the necessary repair, upgrade and replacement work. You could easily end up getting bids from several insulation contractors, hiring a plumber to replace your water heater, bringing in an HVAC contractor to seal ductwork, and arranging for a carpenter to weatherstrip windows and doors.

With Dr. Energy Saver, just one call can do it all. We handle the full range of energy-saving repairs and improvements explained in this book. From air sealing, programmable thermostats, and weatherstripping to HVAC upgrades, insulation, radiant barriers, and many more improvements, we've got the expertise and equipment to transform your house from an energy waster to an energy miser. Dr. Energy Saver has what it takes to go beyond the box to maximize your energy savings.

www.DrEnergySaver.com

17

Energy audits alone *don't* save money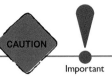

Having an "energy audit" and not moving forward with repairs or retrofits is like going to the Doctor for testing and evaluation, and not doing anything more. You know what the problem is, but you're still sick.

An energy audit is a critical first step in understanding how your house uses energy, loses energy, and wastes money. But most contractors, utilities and companies who perform home energy audits aren't able to follow up and provide all of the energy-saving upgrades that the audit recommends. Just getting a home energy audit and a couple of upgrades (like weatherstripping and new lightbulbs, for example) will not result in significant energy savings. Dr. Energy Saver has the expertise and the resources to perform all of the energy-saving upgrades identified in an energy audit. This comprehensive capability ensures maximum energy savings.

DIYers want to know: "What energy-saving upgrades can I do myself?"

Saving energy is a battle that can and should be waged on many fronts, since there are so many factors that can contribute to energy savings. Some upgrades are suitable for homeowners to tackle, while others are best done by experienced, well-qualified professionals. If you're considering performing some energy-saving upgrades on your own house, ask yourself the following questions:

- **How do I decide what to do first?**

  How much time will it take and do I have the time to spare?

  How quickly can I complete the work?

- **Will I need to buy, borrow or rent specialized equipment to do the job?**

- **Can I do the work safely?**

- **Will the work I do be just as good as what a professional would accomplish?**

- **How much will I save by doing the work myself?**

About our company

Larry Janesky & Tom Casey

Dr. Energy Saver™ was formed when two New England tradesmen got together.

Tom Casey grew up in his family's heating and cooling business, first carrying tools alongside his Dad when he was 11 years old. He took over the business when he was 21, and over the next 22 years, earned industry recognition by winning 10 national awards for comfort and energy conservation projects. Tom was named National Residential Heating and Cooling Contractor of the Year in 2001. Tom's focus on energy savings began long before it caught on in the mainstream.

Larry Janesky started out as a 17-year-old self-employed carpenter. After building over 20 homes, he spent the next two decades building Basement Systems Inc. into the industry-leading company specializing in basement waterproofing, basement finishing, and crawl space repair. Today Basement Systems has over 300 dealers in 6 countries. Larry's interest in building efficiency has lead him to write 3 books – Dry Basement Science, Crawl Space Science, and Basement Finishing Science, and develop an exclusive line of products protected with 25 patents.

Larry has always been interested in efficient building and energy conservation. He hired Tom's company to do an energy assessment on his own home. When Tom found many ways to save energy and money, Larry was excited – and hooked. There are so many people who want to save energy but don't know what to do. Tom and Larry knew that they had to form a company to make energy saving strategies clear and easily available to every homeowner. **Dr. Energy Saver** was born.

Today, **Dr. Energy Saver** is a network of the best energy-conservation contractors across the country who specialize in doing energy and comfort assessments quickly and efficiently. But **Dr Energy Saver** doesn't stop with the assessment; they also do the work, enabling homeowners to get maximum energy and cost-saving results with minimum hassle.

All **Dr. Energy Saver** franchisees are fully trained at the corporate headquarters in Seymour, Connecticut. Thanks to comprehensive training and in-depth support, Tom and Larry's vision for **Dr. Energy Saver** is a sure bet: a company devoted to correcting energy-hogging homes and helping homeowners enjoy more comfort while spending much less on energy.

19

"Who left that window open? *It's freezing in here!*"

You'd be entitled to yell if you found a window left open in your house on a cold winter day. Think of all that warm air escaping, the frigid air coming in, and the furnace needlessly consuming extra fuel and money.

Here's a wake-up call: Many homes have the equivalent of an open window in terms of air leakage, even though all their windows are completely closed. Heat escapes through dozens of small holes, cracks and gaps spread throughout the house, from basement to attic. The combined area of these gaps can easily equal the area of a fully open window.

Dr. Energy Saver says...

Dirt stains on fiberglass attic insulation are a sign of air leakage.

The insulation is filtering the air that leaks out of the living space, trapping dirt and dust just like your furnace filter does. If you see dirt-stained insulation, you know that your house is leaking air.

Mr. and Mrs. Draft were having a spirited discussion (what their children more accurately called an argument) about the comfort level in their house during cold weather. "I don't know what you're talking about," Mr. Draft observed, speaking into his cell phone from an upstairs hallway. "It's toasty warm up here. I can't feel any cold drafts leaking into the house."

"You should come down here," Mrs. Draft replied from the basement laundry room. "You wouldn't believe how chilly it is. And the kitchen right upstairs from where I'm standing isn't much better."

"I don't understand how one part of the house could be so comfortable while another part is cold," Mr. Draft said. "What can we do about this?"

THE STACK EFFECT:

This ★ is a **BIG IDEA!**

Air *leaking* out ➡. ⬅ causes air to *leak* in.

Convection causes the warmest air in your house to rise. Since it's lighter than surrounding air, it wants to keep rising, which is why the greatest amount of air leakage is into the attic, through dozens and dozens of cracks and openings. (We'll get to the origins of these openings in a minute) With air leaking out the top of the house, an equal amount of air is going to come in through openings lower down. Interior air leaks out the top, causing exterior air to enter at the bottom. This is called the stack effect, and it's based on the fact that nature abhors a vacuum.

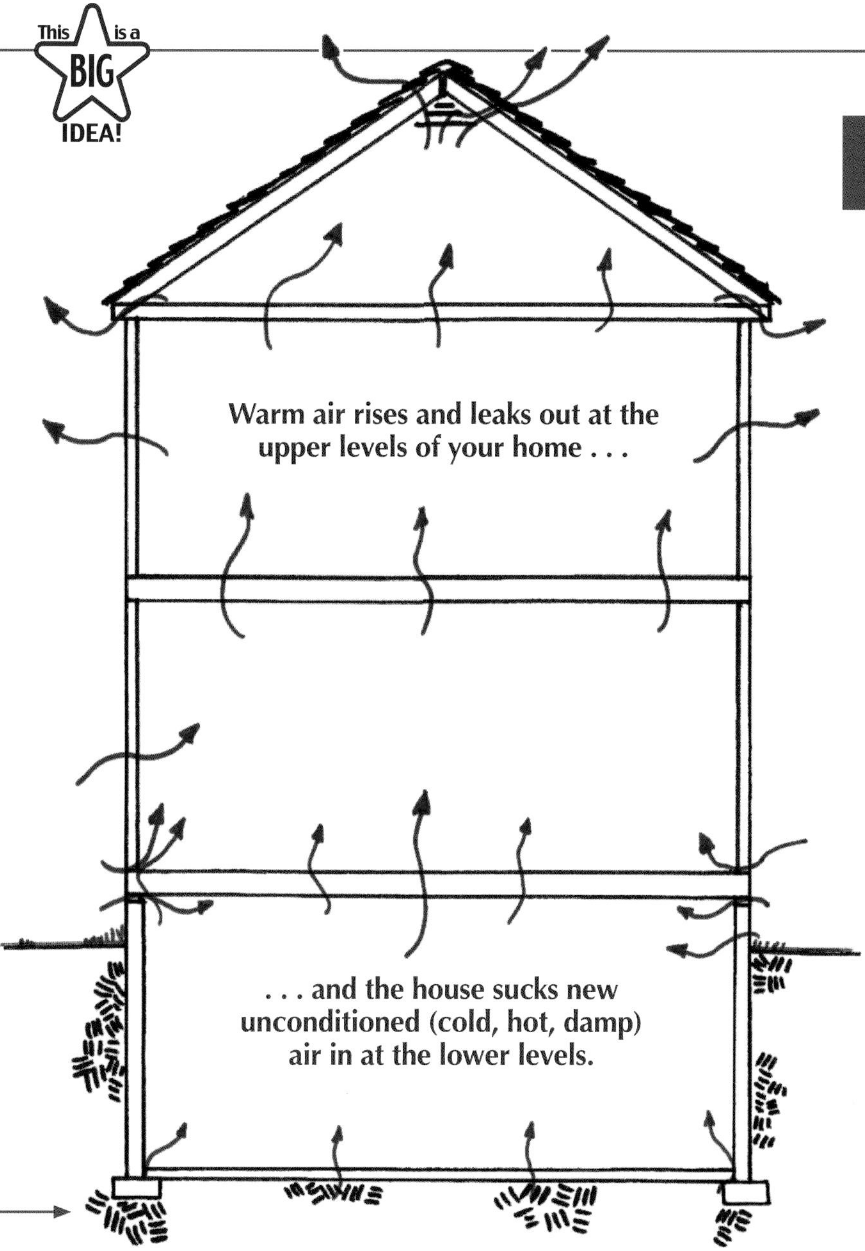

Warm air rises and leaks out at the upper levels of your home . . .

. . . and the house sucks new unconditioned (cold, hot, damp) air in at the lower levels.

21

JOINTS = LEAKS

"How did my house get so leaky?" For starters, a house is made from thousands of parts and pieces, from nails and 2x4s to window casing, electrical wire and drywall panels. Small gaps and cracks occur wherever one part of your house joins another. To make matters worse, many joints that are tight initially don't stay that way. Even before a house is completely built, wood starts to shrink, materials expand and contract at different rates, and connections work loose. Many of these cracks and gaps become leakage points that need to be sealed in order to save energy.

Important

Contractors cause LEAKS *(but they can't help it)*

Leaks are built into the construction process. As soon as the framing crew is finished nailing together all the joists, studs, rafters, beams and sheathing that make up the house shell, other workers come in to start cutting it apart. Plumbers, electricians and HVAC contractors apply their drills and saws to make room so that heating ducts, electrical wires, water lines and waste pipes can be run throughout the house. The resulting holes are normal and don't compromise the strength of a house, but they do create hundreds of leakage points that can allow inside air to leak out and outside air to leak in.

www.DrEnergySaver.com

LEAKS=  LEAKS cost you *money.*

In a house with a lot of air leakage, you're always losing air that you just paid to heat, cool or dehumidify, and replacing it with outside air that needs to be heated, cooled or dehumidified. Air leaks waste energy and make it more costly to keep your house comfortable. Wouldn't you like to enjoy the air you paid to condition a little longer?

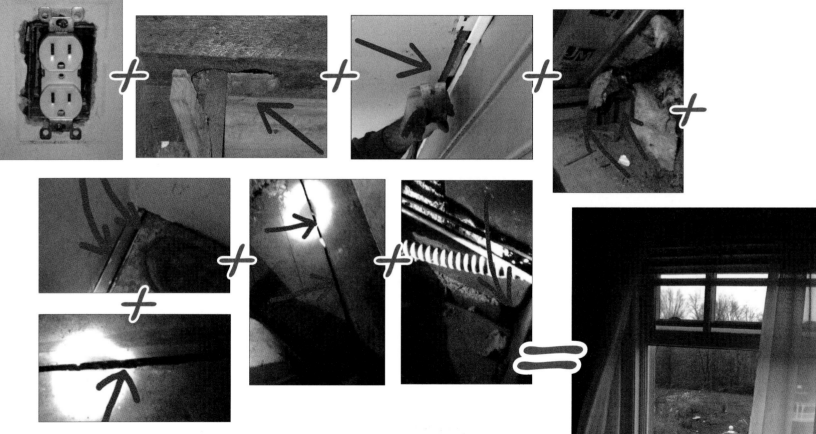

It's like leaving a window open. *Add up the area of all the gaps, cracks and openings where energy can escape in a typical house and you'll easily equal the area of an open window. Gaps can be small, like those around an electrical outlet in an exterior wall. They can be large, like the holes that plumbers often drill in floors and framing to install pipes. And they can be long, like the gap on the outside of the house where the eave soffit is supposed to meet the exterior wall.*

SEALING = $AVING

Sealing leaks in a home's building envelope, a process called air-sealing, increases comfort and energy efficiency while decreasing your fuel bills. Air-sealing can be simply described: Find leaks, then seal them. But this is easier said than done. Finding air leakage demands specialized equipment, skilled detective work and the ability to access parts of the house most homeowners can't easily reach or don't want to. Once leaks are properly identified, it's important to select the right specialty products and use professional techniques to seal them.

Expert leak seekers Dr. Energy Saver technicians know where to look for leaks. But to get a complete picture of how your home leaks and wastes energy, they also use some specialized equipment. An "infiltrometer" or blower door fan is typically placed in the main entry doorway to depressurize the house, or suck out air from the interior. This causes outside air to be drawn into the house through all leakage points. As the fan is running a technician can move from room to room throughout the house to detect and diagnose air leaks.

Blowing smoke is a good thing. *Leaks aren't easy to find. Sometimes they're hidden behind molding or cover plates. They can also be covered by insulation. To detect leaks precisely, Dr. Energy Saver performs a blower door test to suck air out of the house, which draws outside air into the house through leakage points. Smoke tools help to pinpoint leak locations.*

Sometimes it's possible to literally ***see or hear*** where air is coming into the house. But heatless smoke tools are often used to pinpoint leak locations. Technicians may also use a special infrared camera that's super-sensitive to differences in temperature. Surface temperatures show up in contrasting colors, indicating a possible air leak.

In addition to helping the technician detect and diagnose air leaks all over the house, a blower door test also allows your home's air-leakage rate to be calculated. Your Dr. Energy Saver technician can compare the leakage rate (expressed in cubic feet of air per minute) to the size of the house to see how many air changes per hour (ACH) your house could have due to air leakage.

WORKING IN ATTICS – NOT FUN!

Besides being freezing cold in winter and 120° or hotter in the summer, and besides all the fried dust and fiberglass fibers that seem to jump into the air when you touch anything, and besides all the obstacles and tight spaces, and besides having to worry about falling through the drywall ceiling with a single wrong step – attics are great places to work in!

The work of saving energy isn't glamorous or easy, but to get the results you need – that's what Dr. Energy Saver does.

Oh, and crawl spaces are equally fun!

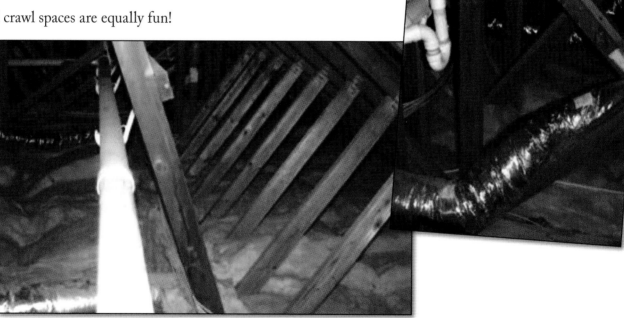

You'll Love This!

Air sealing is a "once-and-done" lifetime repair.
Once you've made this energy-saving upgrade, there's nothing to maintain or replace. You simply keep enjoying the benefits of greater comfort and energy savings forever.

AIR-SEALING STRATEGIES: AS EASY AS A-B-C

1

With the visual inspection and blower door test complete, you should have a pretty good idea of the impact leaks are having on your energy use and comfort. Now what? You're probably wondering: "With so many leaks to plug, where do I start?"

Don't worry. We've got you covered. Dr. Energy Saver's air-sealing strategy provides a simple, common-sense approach to air-sealing your home.

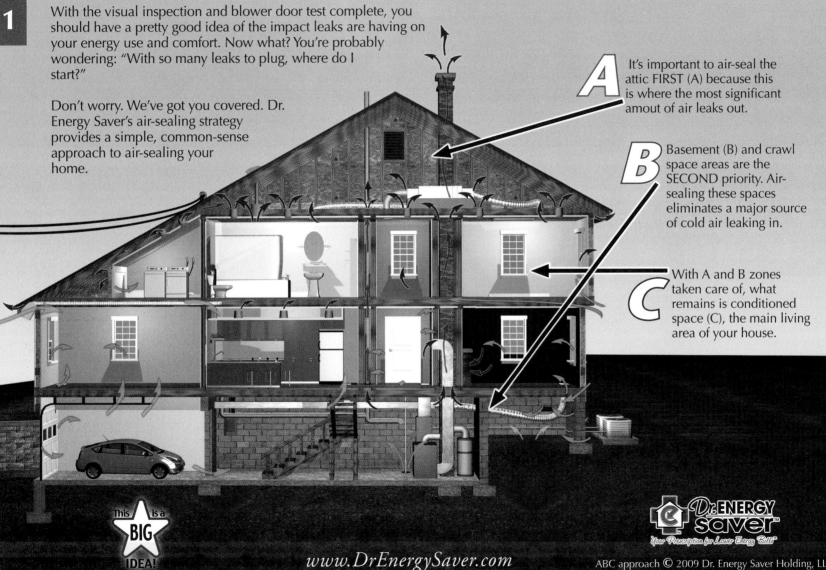

A It's important to air-seal the attic FIRST (A) because this is where the most significant amout of air leaks out.

B Basement (B) and crawl space areas are the SECOND priority. Air-sealing these spaces eliminates a major source of cold air leaking in.

C With A and B zones taken care of, what remains is conditioned space (C), the main living area of your house.

This is a BIG IDEA!

Dr. ENERGY saver
Your Prescription for Lower Energy Bills

www.DrEnergySaver.com

Fiberglass and cellulose insulation will not stop energy-wasting air leaks.
Spray foam insulation is the only type of insulation that can also perform effectively as an air sealer. Air leaks must be sealed before insulating with fiberclass or cellulose

The payoff

You'll Love This!

"Now that I've had air sealing done, I can't wait to see how much more energy efficient my house is going to be."

The excitement is understandable. And if you've had air sealing done by a Dr. Energy Saver crew, you won't have to wait for several months-worth of utility bills to see a difference in energy efficiency. (Obviously, comparing the weather from one month to the last is important to get a meaningful comparison). Dr. Energy Saver technicians perform a second blower door test following the completion of air sealing work. The lower leakage rating will confirm that the house is more airtight, ensuring better energy performance, greater levels of comfort and savings on heating and cooling costs.

An air leak from the basement to the attic is sealed tight.

Air leak to the attic around a pipe is sealed up *forever*.

Air leak at a soffit is sealed to warm floors on second level by stopping unconditioned airflow.

No more leaks! Dr. Energy Saver uses two-part foam for many air-sealing tasks. The mixture leaves the nozzle as a liquid, then expands rapidly to fill and adhere to gaps and cracks. When it cures, the foam creates an airtight barrier that also provides good insulation value.

! M⊘LD

If you have a vented crawl space, a dirt floor crawl space, or a vented AND dirt crawl space, you have been paying higher energy bills than necessary for years.

This is because in the winter the vents let cold/freezing air in – cooling your floors and ducts – *a major problem.*

In the summer, the vents let hot, humid air in, which warms your air conditioning ducts. Even worse, as the moist, warm air enters it condenses on crawl space surfaces, adding moisture to your home. This causes mold, rot, odors, and more load on your air conditioning system, since damp air takes more electricity to cool.

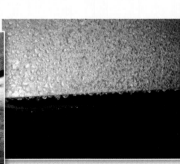

Crawl spaces are easy to ignore since you never go down there. But, studies show, fixing them can save up to 20% in heating and cooling cost

You'll Love This!

The Steps to fix a vented dirt crawl space are:

1 Fix any groundwater problem – with an interior drainage system and a "SmartSump" designed just for crawl spaces.

2 Isolate the house from the earth – with the CleanSpace Encapsulation System. Like a heavy pool liner, it seals up all the walls, and across the floor.

3 Seal all outside air leaks – including vents! Keep unconditioned outside air out! This does wonders for the overall air leakage rate of your house.

4 Dehumidify. Not just any machine will do. A SaniDry CSB Crawl Space Air System is a high-performance machine perfect for the application. Mold doesn't stand a chance!

If you have a dirt crawl space, count on its transformation to be **high on the priority list** after Dr. Energy Saver is done with your Home Energy Check-Up™!

For more complete crawl space information ask for our book: *Crawl Space Science – What to Have Done and Why.*

Crawl Space Science
What to Have Done... *and Why*

Wet Basement? That can affect your home's energy performance, too!

CHAPTER 2 *Insulation*

A T-shirt in a snowstorm?

Spend the winter walking outside in a t-shirt and people will start to question your sanity. But if your home's insulation levels are inadequate, you're doing the same thing on a much larger scale. How did this happen? Well, for one thing, insulation doesn't have the "Wow!" value of crown molding or a fancy chandelier. When electricity and heating fuel were cheap, it made sense for builders to go light on insulation so they could invest in upscale features that homebuyers could see. But fuel is expensive these days, and it's only going to get more costly. Without adequate insulation, your home is going to start draining away dollars that you'd rather spend in other ways. With the right insulation upgrades, you'll be protected from rising energy costs and your house will be more comfortable.

Insulation really works!
A roll of fiberglass insulation or a handful of cellulose insulation may not look like much, but these materials make a big difference in how your home retains heat during the winter and cool air during the summer. Think of how long coffee stays hot when you store it in an insulated Thermos®. That's how your home's insulation can work for you.

The other side of the coin
Proper insulation is just as important for energy savings during **hot weather.** Adding more insulation helps save money on air conditioning and also makes your home more comfortable during hot weather.

What "R" you talking about?

The "R" in R-value stands for resistance to heat flow. The higher the R-value, the higher the resistance and greater the insulating value. When talking about insulation, R-value is typically expressed in two ways:

- **Overall or total R-value.** This number is used as a measure of the total insulation value of a particular product like batts or boards. It's also used to describe the insulation value of a complete building structure, such as a wall that would include studs, plywood sheathing, siding, insulation and drywall.

- **R-value per inch.** Insulation is manufactured from different materials and in different thicknesses. Manufacturers rate their products in terms of R-value per inch, so multiplying the material's R-value per inch by the thickness will give you total R value.

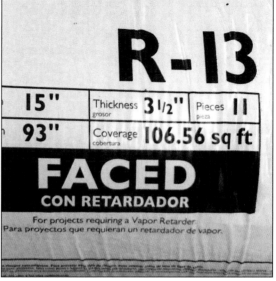

R-13

| 15" | Thickness grosor 3 1/2" | Pieces pieza 11 |
| 93" | Coverage cobertura 106.56 sq ft |

FACED
CON RETARDADOR

For projects requiring a Vapor Retarder
Para proyectos que requieran un retardador de vapor.

Dr. Energy Saver says...

Higher fuel costs = faster payback.

If you're undecided about adding more insulation now, think how you'll feel when fuel prices shoot up again. No matter how you heat and cool your home, the same rule applies: energy upgrades pay for themselves faster as energy costs go up.

SECRET WEAPON

Your Dr. Energy Saver technician can use ***thermographic imagery*** to measure how effectively insulation is working, even when the insulation can't be seen. A special camera provides a picture of a wall, ceiling, or other area that reveals temperature differences by color changes.

Dr. Energy Saver headquarters in Seymour, CT.

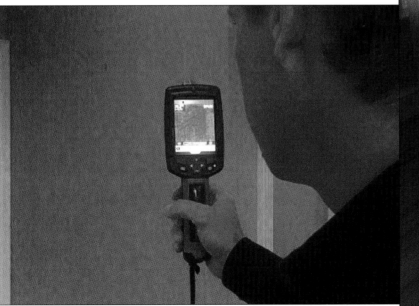

An infared camera clearly reveals missing insulation in the wall...

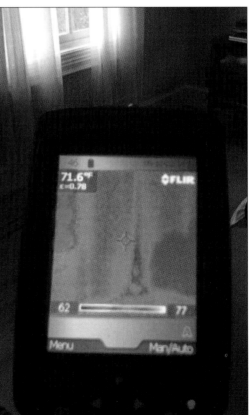

www.DrEnergySaver.com

...and "thermal bridging" in an exterior corner.

How much, what & where?

The general rule of thumb is: The colder your climate, the more insulation you need. Dr. Energy Saver will show you how the current levels of insulation in your house compare with insulation levels recommended by Energy Star and the U.S. Dept. of Energy (see the map).

Recommended insulation levels for retrofitting <u>EXISTING</u> wood-framed buildings

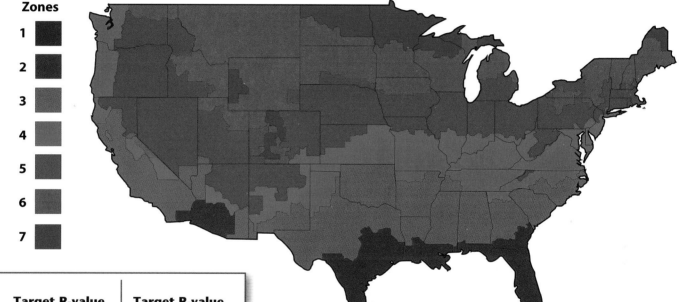

Zones

1
2
3
4
5
6
7

Zone	Target R-value	Target R-value
	Attic insulation	Floor insulation
1	30-49	13
2	30-60	13-19
3	30-60	19-25
4	38-60	25-30
5-8	49-60	25-30

Source: U.S. Dept. of Energy

There are many different types of insulation. Some of the more popular include fiberglass, cellulose and foam. Factors such as availability, affordability and suitability will determine what types are best for your home. Based on Dr. Energy Saver's findings, as well as our proprietary ABC approach, we will recommend insulation upgrades in critical areas of your home's shell.

Common Types of *Insulation*

Cellulose Insulation

(R-3.8 per in.) is made from old newspapers that are shredded and then treated with harmless chemicals to be noncombustible and mold-resistant. Easy to install in attics when a blower unit is used, cellulose can also be blown into wall cavities through holes drilled in siding or interior wallboard. Cellulose has a few drawbacks: It absorbs more moisture than fiberglass, and can take a long time to dry out after wetting. Like all loose-fill insulation, it can blow around if disturbed.

Loose-fill Fiberglass

(R-3.4 per in.) is made from fine glass fibers, just like fiberglass batt insulation. Like cellulose insulation, "shredded" fiberglass is typically installed in attics, using a blower. (Doesn't do anything to slow down air leaks.)

Fiberglass Batts

(R-3.2-3.8 per in.) come in different thicknesses and widths. Unlike loose-fill insulation, batts won't blow or shift around easily. They are easy to move out of the way if you need access to attic framing, wiring, or light fixtures mounted in the ceiling below. Careful installation is required to eliminate energy-wasting airspaces, and installation is more time - consuming because batts must be cut and placed by hand.

Rigid Foam Boards

(R-3.8 to R-8.7 per in.) are available in panels of different sizes and thicknesses. There are three basic types of foam (extruded polystyrene, expanded polystyrene, and polyurethane). Polyurethane foam has the highest R-value. Some foam panels are available with a reflective foil face that can act as a radiant barrier. Although rigid foam is more suitable for new construction, it can be used in retrofit applications, but accurate cutting and fitting are required. Gaps around the edges of rigid foam are often filled with spray foam.

Spray foam:

twice as nice (and 2-3 times the price)

It expands like magic as soon as you apply it. It sticks to everything, including skin and hair. Spray foam is the only insulation that seals as well as insulates, so it often eliminates the need for separate air-sealing steps. Because of its expanding nature, foam excels at filling gaps, cracks, and cavities, eliminating the energy-sapping "voids" that can occur when installing other types of insulation. What's holding foam back from being labeled "the perfect insulation?" You guessed it: cost. You can expect to pay 2-3 times as much for spray foam insulation as you would for fiberglass and cellulose.

Side Note

When insulation is blown into the attic, care must be taken to avoid blocking the soffit vents that are installed along the building's eaves. Before the insulation goes in, special baffles should be installed to keep soffit vents clear.

"What about my old insulation?"

It's sometimes possible to install new insulation over existing insulation. However, at least some of your existing insulation may need to be removed or at least pushed aside so that air-sealing work can be done (see Chapter 1). Dr. Energy Saver will be able to tell you whether your old insulation is worth keeping in place or replacing.

"What about the walls?"

Attics and basements usually remain accessible after a house is built, so it's not a problem to upgrade the insulation in these areas. The same can't be said for walls, since the insulation spaces between studs are hidden behind drywall and exterior siding. Here are three things that Dr. Energy Saver may suggest to upgrade wall energy performance:

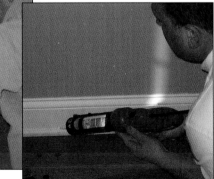

• Start by air-sealing the walls and weatherstripping exterior doors. These two upgrades cost far less than insulating walls, but can still make a significant impact on energy efficiency.

• Blow insulation into wall cavities. It's possible to drill access holes near the top of a wall and blow insulation into wall cavities. Holes are typically drilled from outside. Once the insulation is installed, the holes are plugged as inconspicuously as possible.

• Insulate walls when you're replacing exterior siding. If the siding on the house is in bad shape and will need to be replaced soon, insulation can be added after the old siding is removed.

Dr. Energy Saver says...

Wear a windbreaker with your parka. If you've spent any time outdoors in really cold weather, you know that a down-filled parka and a windbreaker are a good combination. Lightweight but rich in insulation value, the parka's down filling surrounds you with a cushion of warm air. The windbreaker helps to retain your body heat while also blocking the intrusion of cold air – especially on a windy day.

A house can benefit from the same type of protection against energy loss. The air-sealing measures discussed in Chapter 1 act like a windbreaker to keep warm air inside the building envelope and cold air out. Insulation serves as an effective buffer between hot and cold. <u>Air sealing working in combination with insulation</u> will always provide the most significant energy savings.

www.DrEnergySaver.com

Autos and attics

Ever jump in your car after it's been sitting in the sun for an hour or so? Whew! It's REALLY hot. Those dark leather seats can make you jump up when you sit down. How does your car's interior get hotter than the outside air temperature? It's because of the sun's radiant energy –solar heat that keeps building up in the small interior space of your car.

On a sunny summer day, the air in your attic can get just as hot as the air in your car. When attic air temperatures climb to 120°, 130°, 140° and higher, your house heats up, too, causing your air conditioning system to work much harder than it should. You end up using a lot more electricity and paying a lot more to stay comfortable, especially if any portion of your HVAC system or ductwork is in your attic.

FOILING the heat

Spread out beneath your car's windshield, a foil-faced sun shade is a radiant barrier that does a good job of reflecting solar heat so that your car won't get too hot. The radiant barriers used in attics work just like these shiny car shades. During hot weather, an attic radiant barrier can reflect as much as 97% of the sun's heat back toward the outside, reducing your heat gain and lowering air-conditioning costs. In the wintertime, the reflective effect works in reverse, helping to bounce heat back toward your living space.

Give your attic a silver lining

Installing a radiant barrier in your attic is a smart energy-saving investment if you live in a warm climate. But don't rule out this upgrade if you live farther north, especially if you have ductwork and other HVAC equipment (like furnaces or air conditioning units) in your attic. Dr. Energy Saver can install a radiant barrier against the bottom edges of your rafters to help improve cooling efficiency in the summer and heating efficiency in the winter.

The most commonly used radiant barrier for attics is a thin plastic sheet with a reflective finish on one or both sides. Another type of radiant barrier looks just like the bubble wrap used to protect delicate items during shipping, but with a shiny coating. Sheet-type radiant barriers like these can be installed simply by laying them on top of the attic insulation, but they will lose some of their effectiveness over time as dust builds up and reduces the barrier's reflectivity.

Dr. Energy Saver says...

An attic radiant barrier can cut air-conditioning expenses by 10% or more.

You can expect the most savings if you live in warmer climates where AC loads are high - especially if you have ductwork in your attic.

3

You'll Love This!

If you use some of your attic space for storage, have Dr. Energy Saver install a radiant barrier against the rafters. The radiant barrier will protect your stored items from extreme temperatures, and the reflective surface will amplify your attic lighting.

www.DrEnergySaver.com

VENTS HELP YOUR ATTIC
BREATHE

3

MOLD

Good attic ventilation is essential, whether you have a radiant barrier or not. Without good attic ventilation, moisture from the living space can condense and easily build up inside your cold attic space. (By sealing air leaks (Chapter 1) between the ceiling and the attic, you significantly reduce the risk of moisture in the attic.) Damp insulation loses its R-value, and moisture on wood and gypsum board provides ideal conditions for mold to grow. Attic vents also help to let hot air out in the summer to cool the attic. Dr. Energy Saver can assess your attic ventilation as part of an overall energy checkup. Attic ventilation typically consists of a combination of soffit vents (installed along the eaves) and ridge vents, but vents can also be installed in gable ends.

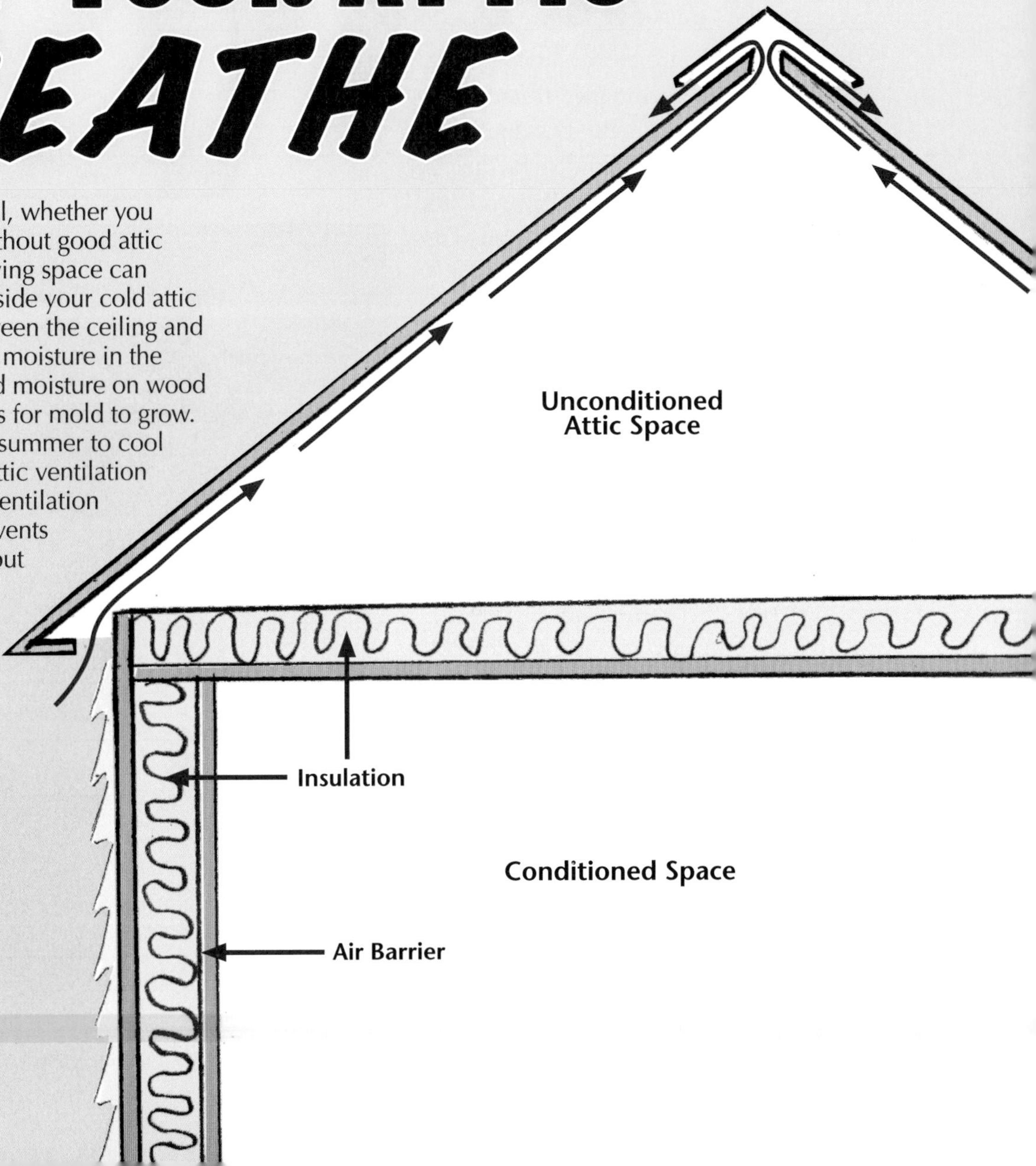

Side Note

Spray foam allows unvented attic assemblies to be constructed these days, but that is a separate and bigger project than the strategies in this book cover.

Unconditioned Attic Space

Insulation

Conditioned Space

Air Barrier

Beware of Attic Fans

Powered attic ventilators (PAVs) are a common "solution" to scorching attic temperatures. These specially designed vent fans mount on the attic roof or in the gable end of the house, and are usually controlled by a thermostat that turns on the fan when the attic reaches a certain temperature. In theory, a PAV is supposed to exhaust hot attic air and pull cooler outside air into the attic space. But in practice, PAVs often suck conditioned air from your living space. Since you don't want to be cooling your attic with air that's supposed to be cooling your house, it's wise to be wary of PAVs. With a radiant barrier in your attic, you have a proven energy-saving feature that doesn't consume any electricity and won't suck away air that you've paid to cool and dehumidify.

Roof mounted attic fan

Wall mounted attic fan

Paint instead of plastic

In some attics, there are too many obstructions that get in the way of installing a sheet-type radiant barrier. Access to certain parts of the attic can also be difficult. In these cases, Dr. Energy Saver may recommend a spray-on radiant barrier. This shiny coating can be applied to the underside of your roof sheathing. While it's not as effective at reflecting heat as a sheet-type barrier, it still does a great job, and may be the most practical way for you to achieve extra energy savings.

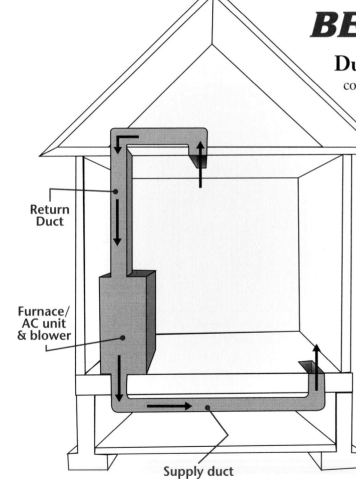

Return Duct

Furnace/ AC unit & blower

Supply duct

BETTER CARE FOR AIR

Ductwork is cool. *Except when it's hot.* If you have central air conditioning, forced-air heating or both, your house contains a ductwork system that distributes conditioned (heated or cooled) air throughout your home. You have supply ducts that "blow" conditioned air to your various rooms, while return ducts suck air back to the furnace or air-conditioning unit so that this air can be heated or cooled and then redistributed. This cycle continues until your thermostat tells your furnace or AC unit that the right temperature has been reached.

Dr. Energy Saver says...

As much as 40% of an HVAC system's energy consumption can be wasted due to faulty or leaky ducts.

That's why it's so important for any home energy checkup to include thorough ductwork testing and evaluation.

www.DrEnergySaver.com

New system, same *old* problem

The Burners finally decided to replace their old heating and cooling system with a new, state-of-the art unit from one of the big-name brands. "You won't believe how much better the new system is going to work, and how much money you're gonna save on your monthly utility bills" their HVAC contractor promised. The new system was much quieter than the old one, and seemed to do an "okay" job of heating and cooling the house, but "much better" wasn't the way the Burners were feeling. And then when the utility bills came, Mr. Burner was –well-- burned up to see that his new system wasn't saving him money.

"What gives?" he asked the contractor. "I thought you said the new system was more energy efficient."

The contractor made several calls and sent multiple technicians to try and see what the problem was, and each time they had the same answer, which was actually no answer at all: "Mr. Burner, the new equipment is working fine, there's nothing wrong." They were nice enough, but they never solved the mystery of the high energy bills.

Mr. Burner's neighbor told him to call Dr. Energy Saver, because they had done a similar project and lowered their bills by 30%. After a visit from Dr. Energy Saver, Mr. Burns learned that his leaky duct system was the culprit, a possibility his previous contractor hadn't even considered. After some careful diagnostic work, the ducts were sealed, the system was balanced, and the Burners finally enjoyed the comfort and energy savings they expected.

WHAT'S AT STAKE:
Sound ductwork makes a *difference*.

Properly sized, properly installed ductwork is critical in any heating and air-conditioning (HVAC) system. Unfortunately, ductwork is *frequently overlooked* when evaluating your home's energy performance, despite its importance. As a result, bad things happen. For example:

• **Comfort:** Leaky supply ducts let air you've paid to heat or cool "leak away" in your attic, basement or crawl space before it gets into your home. Leaky return ducts allow unconditioned air from your attic, basement, or crawl space to "leak into" your system. In both cases, the air that reaches your living space isn't as warm or cool as it's supposed to be, so your comfort is compromised.

• **Energy efficiency:** If conditioned air leaks away before it reaches your living space, obviously you're not getting what you paid for. If air from your hot or cold attic or your freezing basement or crawl space leaks into your system, it takes more energy (and money) to either cool it down or warm it up to make it usable for your living space. You could be cooling or heating the great outdoors without even realizing it!

• **Indoor air quality:** If you have return duct leaks, you could be pumping "bad air" directly into your living space when your system runs. You wouldn't want to breathe crawl space or attic air all day, but if you have duct leakage, you might be! Leaky ducts also cause indoor air quality problems because of "pressure imbalances" that put some rooms or areas under positive pressure and others under negative pressure. This causes unhealthy air (laden with dirt, dust, pollen, allergens, and other contaminants) to be sucked into your home.

• **Safety:** Pressure imbalances caused by leaky ducts can cause backdrafting in combustion appliances such as furnaces, wood stoves, water heaters and gas ranges. When this happens, you risk exposure to carbon monoxide, a deadly gas.

4

Don't **FORCE** your HVAC system to **RUN** in place

You're legs are pumping, your feet are pounding the pavement, you're huffing and puffing, _but it doesn't feel like you're going anywhere_. That's what it's like for your HVAC system if you have leaky ducts. Let's take a closer look: Your system turns on to keep your home comfortable, and the fan kicks on to start circulating air. As soon as the fan gets up to speed, your leaky return ducts start to suck in air from your hot attic or cold basement or crawl space. Instead of dealing with air returning from your house at indoor temperatures, your system encounters unconditioned air that's much hotter or colder. Your furnace or air conditioner has to work extra hard to make this air the right temperature. Okay, that's bad, but that's only the half of it. Now you've got air that's not quite "cold enough" or "warm enough" traveling down your supply duct system, and your leaky supply ducts let some of this air (which you've already overpaid to heat or cool) leak out instead of delivering it to your home. As a result, your system needs to be larger and run longer and you have uncontrolled "bad air" leaking into your living space. Your allergies flare up, and your house is dirtier and dustier, too. Sealed ductwork is <u>very</u> important.

Balancing supply & return

WHAT GOES IN = WHAT GOES OUT

Efficient HVAC performance depends on balanced air flow. The air volume your system returns from your house should equal the air volume your system supplies to it. If one is greater than the other, there is an air pressure imbalance.

Negative pressure in a room can act like a vacuum, pulling air into the room from outside or from "bad" sources like a crawl space or attic. Drafty or uncomfortable rooms may be the result of imbalanced airflows.

Different types of ducts - but they ALL can leak.

Sheet metal. Made from galvanized steel, these ducts can be rectangular or round. One duct section usually slides into another. Leaks occur where sections join together.

Fiberglass duct board. Often used to form large-section trunk lines that feed smaller ducts, fiberglass duct board is insulated (around R4.5 for 1-in.-thick board) and has a smooth finish to promote good air flow. It has a shiny silver color on the outside. Its porous inner surface is hard to clean, and its taped connections are prone to leaking.

Building cavities. In some homes the open bays between wall studs and floor joists are often used as part of a home's ductwork system. Taking advantage of building cavities is an attractive option for builders because it saves money. This type of duct leaks significantly depending on the assembly, and often directly connects your system to sources of bad air.

Flexible nonmetallic ducts. These vinyl wire-reinforced ducts have enough flexibility to snake around obstacles. Flex ducts are popular because they are less expensive and easier to install. Longer lengths can eliminate the need for many joints, but leaks can still occur where the flex duct joins sheet metal registers or other types of ductwork. Flex ducts can be torn, cut and crushed easily, so careful handling is important.

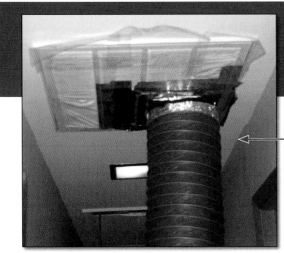

"Duct blaster" test measures energy-wasting duct leakage.

Dr. ENERGY saver™ can:

diagnose duct leakage problems. . .

It takes the right tools and good diagnostic skills to detect duct leakage and other duct problems. When Dr. Energy Saver tests your ductwork system, you will see instantly how you are losing energy and wasting money. You'll also find out if your ductwork system is causing pressure imbalances that can encourage outside air to leak into your house.

. . . and seal them!

What follows after leak detection is leak sealing. The best sealing strategy for your ductwork depends not only on the type of ductwork, but also on the accessibility of the leaking ducts. Dr. Energy Saver has the right tools, specialized materials and professional techniques to do a sealing job that's effective and durable to improve your comfort and indoor air quality while also saving you money!

Sealing a new duct with duct mastic.

Duct leaks under the grilles

Under supply grilles or return "registers", where the duct meets the finished surface of the floor, wall, or ceiling, there is a "joint" or connection. These joints can leak air to or from the wrong places significantly, increasing operating costs and decreasing indoor air quality. Sealing theses spaces is all part of saving energy and money.

Only a *quack* would use "DUCK TAPE" on DUCTWORK

Duct tape has thousands of uses, *but it shouldn't be used on ductwork.* This tape was originally developed during World War II to keep moisture out of ammunition cases. Servicemen appreciated the tape's waterproof qualities and the fact that the cloth backing was made from cotton duck cloth, so the name "duck tape" was coined. After the war, duck tape became "duct tape" when contractors began using it to seal ductwork. But time has taught us that duct tape dries out and disintegrates when used on ductwork. Its sealing effectiveness doesn't last very long. Duct tape is handy to have around; just don't use it for sealing leaky ducts.

> *"duct tape dries out and disintegrates when used on ductwork."*

4

How about blowing heated air through a refrigerator?
Ducts need insulation, too!

Without adequate insulation, the conditioned air that you paid to heat or cool travels through your ductwork with little or no protection against extreme air temperatures. Imagine a sheet metal duct system in a sweltering attic on a hot summer day. How much do you think cool conditioned air might warm up as it flows through hot ducts? Or, how about heated air running through ducts in a freezing crawl space or attic? How much do you think this heated air will cool down as it passes through freezing ductwork? These energy losses can really add up fast, and they have a negative effect on comfort as well as energy efficiency.

Adding insulation can help to reduce energy losses in duct runs. Dr. Energy Saver will know the best type of insulation, as well as the proper insulation levels to use to make your ductwork more energy efficient.

THE HIGHER CO$T OF COMFORT

For many years, the cost of electricity, natural gas and heating oil was low enough so that we didn't have to worry about our monthly utility bills. But today's growing global demand for energy has caused electricity and fuel prices to skyrocket, and this is just the beginning. Increased global demand and dwindling supply will push fuel prices ever higher. Because heating and cooling account for almost half of your household energy budget, it's critical for your heating and air conditioning (HVAC) systems to work as efficiently as possible.

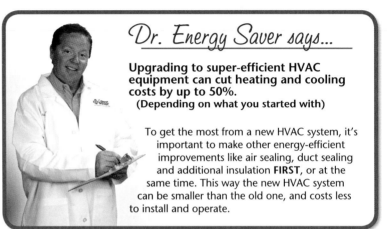

Dr. Energy Saver says...

Upgrading to super-efficient HVAC equipment can cut heating and cooling costs by up to 50%.
(Depending on what you started with)

To get the most from a new HVAC system, it's important to make other energy-efficient improvements like air sealing, duct sealing and additional insulation **FIRST**, or at the same time. This way the new HVAC system can be smaller than the old one, and costs less to install and operate.

You can't get high efficiency *out of a low efficiency machine.*

"**HVAC**" means
Heating
Ventilating and
Air
Conditioning

The older your HVAC equipment is, the lower its efficiency. Technology has advanced and new HVAC equipment is MUCH better at converting fuel or electricity to hot or cold air for your home. Even equipment as little as 12 years old would be considered antique compared to new state-of-the-art equipment. Sure it's an investment, but if you are going to pay for it whether you get it or not, you may as well get it!

What kind of mileage are you aiming for? In terms of energy efficiency, an old HVAC system is like a vintage vehicle that can only get 12 miles per gallon. Modern HVAC equipment is just as miserly with electricity and fuel as a hybrid car is with gasoline.

Size really *does* matter
(and bigger is NOT better)

Have you already improved your home's energy efficiency with air-sealing (Chapter 1), additional insulation (Chapter 2), and duct sealing (Chapter 4) If so, you'll be amazed at how much smaller your HVAC equipment can be. Bigger is definitely not better when it comes to heating and cooling your house. Dr. Energy Saver will make sure that a new HVAC system is sized to match your home's improved energy profile.

Dirty air filter

The easiest way to save money and avoid disaster

Dirt is the #1 cause of HVAC system inefficiency. It's also the most common cause of a system breakdown or failure. Having your heating or cooling system professionally tuned-up every spring and fall is critical to saving energy. It also ensures smooth operation and helps you avoid a premature failure that could cost you thousands of dollars. Even a new HVAC system should be regularly serviced to maintain the efficiency you paid for. **Just like anything mechanical, your system's efficiency begins to degrade the moment you start to operate it, so planned professional maintenance, that includes a lot more than just changing the filters, is your sure way to keep your system in tip-top shape**. Dr. Energy Saver will check your system's critical components and make sure they're functioning safely and efficiently.

Comparing common types of HVAC systems

These brief descriptions will give you a basic idea of the how different heating and air conditioning systems work. Some heating and air conditioning systems perform better in certain climates than they do in others. Dr. Energy Saver will evaluate your system and give you the details on how it can be improved for better performance and energy savings.

Forced-air heating systems *(a.k.a furnaces)* burn fossil fuel (oil or gas) to heat the air. A central fan blows this air through supply ductwork to distribute it throughout your living space. Return ductwork delivers air back to the unit to be reheated and redistributed. Forced air heating is affordable and offers the advantage of a ductwork system that can also be used for central air conditioning.

Hydro-air is a variation on forced-air heating. A boiler (gas or oil-fired) heats water that is pumped through a heat exchanger or coil mounted in your ductwork. Air passes through the coil to pick up heat before it's distributed throughout the home. The boiler in a hydro-air system often does double duty, heating water for washing and for heating. This eliminates the need for a separate water heater.

Hot water baseboard heat relies on a boiler to heat water. The hot water gets pumped to baseboard or other types of radiators that are mounted on the wall. This type of heating system requires no ductwork, which is both good (no leaky ducts to worry about) and bad (no distribution system for central air conditioning). Most common in northern climates.

5

An air-source heat pump is a central air conditioner that can run in "reverse," supplying hot air in the winter and cool air in the summer. If you're ever waved your hand over your AC unit outside on a hot day while it's cooling your house, you probably noticed the outdoor unit was blowing hot air. During cold weather, this cycle is reversed to move heat into the house.

A geothermal or ground-source heat pump works like its cousin, the air source heat pump, with one major distinction: It relies on the earth's ground energy to either dump its heat (summer) or pick it up (winter). Because the earth's temperature remains about the same (55°-65° F) 6-12 ft. below the surface, this type of heat pump performs efficiently in all climates. See Chapter 11 for more information.

Combi systems supply hot water for heating and also for bathing and washing. Typically compact and very energy efficient, these systems are popular in Europe where energy costs are very high, and space is at a premium. Combi systems burn fossil fuel, and usually can supply virtually any form of hydronic heating application.

Radiant floor heat puts the warmth under your feet. Warm water from a boiler is pumped through tubing installed beneath the finished floor surface. The flooring material is heated, and acts like a giant radiator, warming objects rather than the air. This type of heating system is comfortable and energy efficient.

Hybrid heating systems: By combining an air source heat pump with a fossil fuel furnace, or hydro air, this system gives you the flexibility to use the most cost-effective fuel at any given time or temperature. In addition, you get built-in redundancy so that if one system isn't working correctly, the other can take over. Controls are automated so there's nothing for you to do once you have programmed the thermostat.

The big payoff:
a smaller HVAC system

If you're in the market for a new system, the first thing Dr. Energy Saver will do is determine the size of the unit that's required. Your heating and air-conditioning requirements are based on numerous factors including house size and orientation, the number and type of windows, how much air leakage and insulation your home has, and different lifestyle factors. If you integrate air-sealing, duct sealing/repairs and insulation upgrades with Dr. Energy Saver, you're about to get a BIG payoff: Your new HVAC system can be smaller in capacity than the equipment you're replacing. It will be less costly upfront to replace your old system, and less expensive to operate, too.

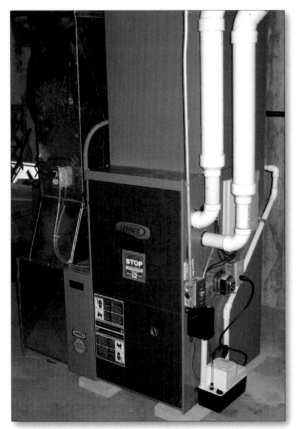

Gas Heating / Air Conditioning System

The common practice of oversizing heating and cooling systems can cause you to overpay to install a new system and overpay every month to keep it working. Believe it or not, HVAC systems have traditionally been sized to handle the worst 1% of weather in a specific location, which means that 99% of the time the system is simply too big! To make matters worse, system designers often add safety factors as high as 10% to make absolutely, positively sure your system isn't too small. As a result, you pay more upfront and every month. Dr. Energy Saver can help you avoid this expensive mistake by right-sizing your heating and cooling systems based on integrated energy conservation approaches. You'll save money now and for the life of your HVAC system.

www.DrEnergySaver.com

Alphabet Soup: Sorting out efficiency ratings.

Today all new furnaces, boilers, air conditioners and heat pumps come with standardized efficiency ratings. Like the estimated MPG ratings for new cars, higher numbers indicate greater energy efficiency. Ratings used for HVAC equipment are a bit more complicated because different rating systems are used for different types of equipment. The list below explains what the acronyms stand for, and how they relate to different types of HVAC equipment. Dr. Energy Saver can identify your best options for improving energy efficiency with new HVAC equipment.

Rating Acronym	What it stands for	Comments
AFUE	Annual Fuel Use Efficiency	used for furnaces, boilers and water heaters. An AFUE of 90% means you get 90 cents of usable heat for every $1-worth of fuel burned. The higher the AFUE, the lower your heating costs. Energy Star qualified furnaces and boilers rate 85% AFUE or higher. AFUE ratings are slightly lower for water heaters, depending on fuel.
SEER	Seasonal Energy Efficiency Rating	applies to overall efficiency of AC equipment under different operating modes over an entire season. Efficient models typically rate 16 SEER or higher.
COP	Coefficient of Performance	a ratio of energy output versus energy input, normally used to describe heat pump performance under specific operating conditions.
HSPF	Heating Seasonal Performance Factor	rates the efficiency of air source heat pumps. This is basically the average COP for an entire heating season. Efficient heat pumps typically rate 9 HSPF or higher.

5

A *"smart"* thermostat puts your home on *cruise control*

☑ Control

☑ Comfort

☑ Cost savings

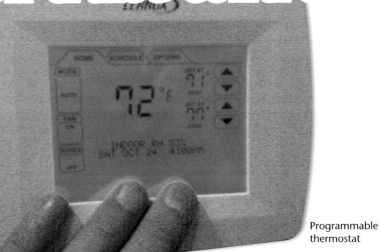

Programmable thermostat

Wouldn't it be great if your heating or cooling system automatically turned down at night while you slept, and automatically came on again just before you woke up every morning? How about having your HVAC system automatically switch between weekday and weekend modes, keeping the HVAC action going while you're at home, but turning it up or down while you're out during the week?

Dr. Energy Saver can make this level of control possible by installing a programmable thermostat. These devices are like mini-computers, storing time and temperature settings based on your daily schedule. You can tell your HVAC system when you need comfortable indoor temperatures and when the system can "relax" because you're out of the house. Settings are also easy to override if your schedule changes. Try it, you'll like it: increased energy and cost savings, decreased anxiety. You won't be driving down the road wondering if you remembered to adjust the thermostat or not. Instead you'll be able to set it and forget it, with your comfort and energy savings on cruise control.

www.DrEnergySaver.com

Mrs. Spore was frustrated. "Why does our bathroom have a moldy smell?" she asked her husband.

"I don't know what the problem is," her husband replied. "We have an exhaust vent fan in the bathroom so we shouldn't have moisture problems."

The case of the mysterious mold smell was solved during an Energy Savings Check-Up™. While inspecting the attic, Dr Energy Saver noticed that the bathroom fan vented directly into the attic space instead of to the outside like it's supposed to. As soon as the warm, moist bathroom air hit the cold attic, moisture was condensing out of the air, soaking the nearby insulation, wood and drywall, providing perfect conditions for mold growth.

Moving moist air ALL the way outside

Fortunately, the Spores' moisture problem was detected and corrected before it got too severe. Dr. Energy Saver installed a new, high-efficiency bathroom fan that not only moved more air for improved ventilation, it also operated more

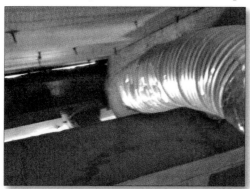

A vent hose not ducted all the way out. You can see the water stains.

quietly than the original fan. After removing the damp insulation and air-sealing the attic, Dr. Energy Saver installed new insulation and properly vented the fan to the outside.

To avoid serious moisture and mold problems, bathroom and kitchen vent fans as well as the dryer vent must all be vented to the outside of your house. Pushing the open end of a vent's flexible duct into the soffit (a common shortcut used by some contractors) is not good enough and will lead to problems. Dr. Energy Saver will make sure that your clothes dryer and exhaust/ vent fans are properly vented to the outside.

Little black boxes... Okay, they're not *always* black

Your existing heating and cooling system can be made more efficient if Dr. Energy Saver adds specialized microprocessor controls designed to optimize system performance. Sometimes these controls utilize an outdoor temperature sensor and/ or a living space temperature sensor to anticipate your home's heating or cooling needs and efficiently control your systems based on specific algorithms. If your system is newer, or if you're not ready to retire an older HVAC system, Dr. Energy Saver can add an optimizer control to make your existing system operate more efficiently until you're ready for a new system. And the great thing is, you can re-use your optimizer control when you do replace your system. It's a little investment that saves big all year long.

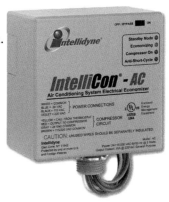

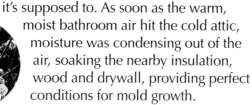

5

CHAPTER 6 *Water Heating*

Out of **sight**, out of **mind**

Your water heater is the classic strong, silent type. Day in and day out, it delivers the steady supply of hot water you **rely** on for washing clothes, bathing and cleaning dishes. Hidden away in the back of a utility closet or a dark corner of your basement, your water heater is easy to overlook until you realize that it can account for a whopping 15% of your total energy usage. Improvements in water heating have the potential to *save you hundreds of dollars* a year or more, depending on how many people live in your home.

15% of your **total** energy usage

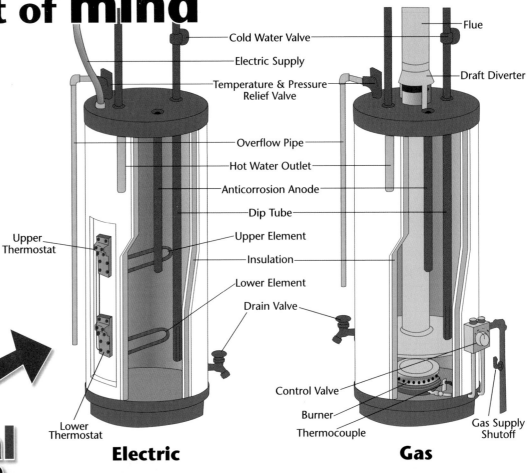

Cold Water Valve

Electric Supply

Temperature & Pressure Relief Valve

Flue

Draft Diverter

Overflow Pipe

Hot Water Outlet

Anticorrosion Anode

Dip Tube

Upper Thermostat

Upper Element

Insulation

Lower Element

Drain Valve

Lower Thermostat

Control Valve

Burner

Thermocouple

Gas Supply Shutoff

Electric

Gas

Old School

A traditional tank-style water heater is really nothing more than a big metal container of water that gets heated by either electrical elements or fossil fuel. When you open a tap or use hot water in your home, water you've paid to heat travels through hot water supply lines to its point of use. At the same time, cold water flows into your tank to replace the heated water that just left. The larger your hot water tank, the more hot water you can use before running out.

Tank-style water heaters represent old-fashioned technology that hasn't changed much in decades. Your water heater normally has a 5-10-year manufacturer's warranty, which is about the life expectancy before problems can start to develop. Even a water heater that's 15 years old can still provide plenty of hot water and appear to be in good operating condition, but looks can be deceiving. It is probably wasting energy because of inadequate insulation and low efficiency, plus there may be problems inside that you can't see.

A Flood Waiting to Happen

The reality is that tank-type water heaters fail gradually, and then suddenly. One day you've got a flood on your hands that could cause thousands of dollars in damages, not to mention the longer term issues of mold or mildew that might result. Corrosion and sediment inside your tank steadily diminish your tank's heating efficiency and eventually lead to leaks, whether it's a slow drip or a catastrophic failure. The water inside your water heater is under 50-60 pounds per square inch of pressure. When a water heater leaks, it's not just the water inside of it that leaks out. Since the tank automatically fills again, the leak never stops until you notice it and shut the water (and heater) down. Water heater leaks are the number one homeowner insurance claim. Dr. Energy Saver will inspect your water heater during your

Energy Savings Check-Up™. If your water heater is ready to be retired, there's good news: Installing a new Energy Star model can cut your overall energy bill by 10% or more. For even more savings, consider a tankless water heater (see page 60).

It's a wrap

Try this test: Touch the outside of your water heater. If you feel warmth, your water heater is losing heat that you paid for to the surrounding air. This is known as standby heat loss. It causes the water inside the tank to cool so that it has to be reheated over and over again, a cycle that wastes energy 24/7, 365 days a year whether you're home or not, awake or not, or using hot water or not. Water heaters that have an Energy Star rating are manufactured with high levels of tank insulation to minimize standby heat loss, but they don't eliminate it completely. If you don't have an Energy Star water heater, Dr. Energy Saver can wrap your tank with extra insulation to cut down on standby heat loss.

www.DrEnergySaver.com

6

A simple way to $ave: turn down the heat

If you have a tank-type water heater, there's a good chance you can save money simply by lowering your water heater's thermostat setting. At the factory, manufacturers can set a water heater's thermostat as high as 140 degrees. That's about 20 degrees higher than necessary. If you need to cool down your hot water by turning on the cold water faucet, that means that you're paying extra to overheat your water.

Dr. Energy Saver can test your water temperature and make the appropriate adjustments for you. For each 10°F reduction in water temperature, you can save between 3%–5% in water heating costs.

3-5% savings!

Pipe insulation pays off

Whenever you use hot water, it flows from your water heater through a network of plumbing pipes to the faucet or fixture you're using. When you turn off the faucet, there's still a supply of hot water sitting in your pipes. Without pipe insulation, that hot water quickly gives up its heat to the surrounding air – another case of standby heat loss. Uninsulated hot water lines waste water as well as energy, since you need to keep the water running until the hot water arrives. It's also aggravating to wait around for hot water.

Insulating your hot water lines is such a smart, affordable energy upgrade that it falls into the "no-brainer" category. To do this job right, it's important to select the proper insulation materials, size them to match your plumbing, and install the pipe insulation properly. *Dr. Energy Saver can perform this energy - saving upgrade so that you can minimize standby heat loss and enjoy more energy savings.*

6

Yank the Tank... and save BIG

How big? If you replace a tank-type water heater with a tankless model, you could cut your water heating bill by as much as 45%!

45% savings!

The tankless water heater is the best thing to happen to heating water since water heaters were invented. Also known as a "demand heater," a tankless water heater saves energy and money simply because of how it works. Unlike an old-fashioned tank-style heater that consumes energy heating and re-heating your water even when you're not using it, a tankless heater only heats water once, when you call for it. If your house is empty all day, when you're on vacation, when you're asleep at night, a tankless water heater just sits and waits, consuming zero energy. It turns on when you turn on the hot water faucet, the washing machine, the shower or other hot water fixture.

Here are the key details:

▶ Tankless water heaters are available in fossil fuel or electric versions, with the highest efficiencies being realized with natural gas and propane models.

▶ Tankless water heaters are compact --about the size of a carry-on bag. A typical model can mount on a wall just about anywhere. Installation locations are flexible, especially since there's no need to worry about leaks or flooding. Gas-fired models need to be vented to the outside.

▶ Many tankless units have the Energy Star rating and qualify for rebates, tax credits or other incentives.

▶ Tankless water heaters only operate when you are actually using hot water, and they typically modulate their capacity to match the amount of water flowing. If you're washing out a cup versus taking a shower, the heater automatically operates at the most efficient setting.

▶ Because of their ability to match output to actual hot water demand, tankless water heaters are very good at meeting multiple demands simultaneously. You never run out of hot water like you do with a tank-style water heater.

▶ Some tankless units can even serve two purposes by combining hot water heating with space heating.

You'll Love This!

Save $ and Space

Tankless water heaters are small and mount on the wall, freeing up the space where your old tank-type water heater is for storage or usable space.

6

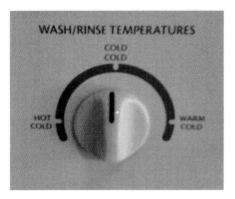

Who wants a cold shower?

Yes, there are limits to what we're willing to do in order to save energy. Most of us would agree that taking cold showers is taking things too far. But that's not true for your clothes. Up to 85% of the energy consumed during a washing machine's cycle is used for heating water. So unless you're dealing with oily stains, it makes sense to use a laundry detergent designed for cold water, and keep the dial on your machine set to cold water for washing and rinsing.

up to 85% of energy consumed during one wash cycle is used to HEAT water.

Well water tanks need insulation, too!

Why? Well water is 55° when it comes out of the ground. You want to heat your home to 70°, a 15° difference. Without insulation, heat from your home will forever be absorbed by the cold well water - wasting energy. Insulating the well water tank will save energy and help prevent condensation on the tank in the summertime.

You'll Love This!

Because tankless water heaters are much more compact than tank-style water heaters, there's more flexibility in locating a tankless unit.

By locating a tankless heater close to a bathroom, you can shorten the hot water supply line and make the arrival of hot water just about *instantaneous*.

6

North America at night from space

Getting the light RIGHT

There's a lot to like about the original energy-efficient light source: inexpensive, zero electricity use, excellent portability, and a breeze to turn off. It's a good thing that most households still keep candles on hand. But it's also good that we've developed artificial light in many forms. We depend so much on lamps and light fixtures that **lighting accounts for 15% of a typical household electric bill**. The good news here is that by taking advantage of the latest lighting technology, you can reduce your lighting bill by 50%-75%. That's major savings.

Dr. Energy Saver says...

What's good for your house is also good for the country.

If every household in the U.S. switched to energy-efficient lighting, we'd save enough electricity to shut down 90 power plants! And in a single year, our reduction of greenhouse gas emissions would be like taking 800,000 cars off the road.

www.DrEnergySaver.com

Speedy savings with just a *few good turns*

Replacing your old-fashioned incandescent light bulbs with high-efficiency compact fluorescent light bulbs (CFLs) is a fast, effective way to save energy and lower your monthly electric bill. In fact, having Dr. Energy Saver replace your inefficient incandescent lights with CFLs will pay for itself faster than any energy upgrade.

◀ **A "CFL" Compact Fluorescent Light Bulb**

CFLs save in several ways:

• **Greater efficiency.** CFLs are about 75% more efficient than incandescent lighting at converting the electricity you pay for into light.

• **Longer life.** A CFL will last about 10 times longer than your incandescent light bulbs.

• **CFL's are Cool.** A typical CFL operates at just 90 degrees vs. 350 degrees for incandescent bulbs. Heat has always been an inefficient by-product of incandescent technology. With CFLs, you're not paying for extra electricity that gets converted into heat instead of light. And in the summer, your air conditioning system will run less to get rid of the heat from your lighting! (This may cause you to think that heat from lighting is good during the heating season. The problem is it's much more expensive heat than you want.)

When does 13=60?

Check out how little electricity a CFL requires to produce light equivalent to common incandescent light bulbs:

13-watt CFL = 60-watt incandescent
18-watt CFL = 75-watt incandescent
26-watt CFL = 100-watt incandescent

www.DrEnergySaver.com

Thanks, Tom

Thomas Edison once said he **didn't fail** 10,000 times at inventing the light bulb. He simply **learned** 10,000 ways not to make a light bulb before successfully accomplishing what is perhaps one of the most important inventions of the 20th century.

7

All shapes & sizes

Because CFLs operate on a different technology than incandescent lights, they look different, too. The most familiar CFL is a small spiral version designed to screw into a standard light fixture. But quite a few other fluorescent bulbs are also available. Dr. Energy Saver has a full selection of CFLs to meet all your lighting needs. CFLs have come a long way, and no longer produce the ghostly colored light they once did. You probably won't be able to tell the difference and if you do, you'll get used to it in a couple days and forget about it as you save.

You'll Love This!

up to
$120
savings/year

Do the math

You could save as much as $120 a year if you have Dr. Energy Saver replace 10 standard 60-watt incandescent light bulbs and 5 100-watt bulbs with equivalent CFLs. Over the life of your new CFLs, you could save more than $650!

Every CFL you install or have installed can save you over $100 over the life of the bulb.

"The Math"

If you replace one 100 watt incandescent bulb with a 23 watt CFL.

100 - 23 = 77 watts saved

77 Watts x 10,000 hours (life of a CFL) = 770,000 watt hours saved.

770,000 ÷1000 = 770 killowatt hours

770 x 16¢* cost per killowatt hour = $123.20

You save $123.20 for each bulb changed, over its life!

*Electricity rates vary from 11¢ to 20¢ throughout the United States

7

Safe handling is important: A CFL contains a tiny amount of mercury, which can be toxic. There's no danger of exposure unless a bulb is broken, so it's smart to treat the CFLs in your house with care to avoid breaking a bulb. If you do break a bulb, don't vacuum it up. Instead, use lengths of duct tape to pick up dust and fragments, wipe the area with a damp paper towel, and put all waste material into a plastic bag. Call your local sanitation department to find out where the waste can be delivered.

Can you change bulbs yourself?
Of course! Go for it. But, if you want to save the trouble, Dr. Energy Saver can do it for you. Ceiling fixtures may require a ladder, and some fixtures may require tools. Be sure to select the right wattages and shape and style bulbs (interior, exterior, dimmable, non-dimmable, etc.)

Important

LED Bulbs
The way of the future!

Look out for LEDs
5 times more efficient than CFLs

We're talking about Light-Emitting Diodes, which are likely to replace CFLs someday as the leading products in energy-efficient lighting. LEDs have no mercury, and are tiny compared to incandescent and fluorescent lights, because no filament is required in the bulb. Instead, current passes through a tiny semiconductor, exciting electrons to produce light. In case you're wondering what an LED light looks like, you've already seen plenty of them – on digital clocks, watches, calculators, and appliance control panels. As for LED light bulbs for all your fixtures, these aren't commonly available yet as an affordable alternative to CFLs. One LED bulb costs $100 today! (2009) But that's certain to change as technology catches up with the demand for more efficient products.

www.DrEnergySaver.com

Kicking the (old) can

Recessed "can" lights are very popular, and most homes have at least some of these ceiling lights in one part of the home or another. The trouble with recessed lights is that when they are installed in the upper ceiling below the attic, they waste energy in several ways:

• **Air leakage.** Air that you've paid to heat or cool can leak out of your living space into the attic through gaps around the light fixture or in the fixture itself.

• **Absent insulation.** If your recessed lights do not have an "IC" rating, this means that insulation can't come in contact with the fixture, so you can be sure you're losing energy around each non-IC light fixture.

• **Light leakage.** Some of your recessed fixtures may not have the proper reflectors to effectively reflect light downward. If you've ever seen light spilling out of a can light that's on while you're up in the attic, this means that some of the light you're paying for is going where it's not needed.

Dr. Energy Saver will evaluate your can lights as part of an overall Energy Savings Check-Up™. If your existing can lights are wasting energy in any of these ways, it may make sense to retrofit them, replace them, or build an airtight box around them in the attic.

Recessed can lights are full of holes, and allow your heated air to leak to the attic and be lost.

Dimmers make a difference

Replacing your standard wall-mounted light switch with a dimmer switch can save you energy by allowing you to operate lights at lower power levels. Dimmers also help your light bulbs last longer. Of course another benefit is the control you gain over adjusting the mood of a room simply by moderating your light levels. Dr. Energy Saver can assess your lighting to see if dimmers would save electricity while providing useful control of light levels in different parts of your house. Since CFLs are now available in dimmable versions, you can save electricity and have adjustable light levels as well.

7

Motion-sensing switches save time and *energy!*

How many times have you walked through your house and found the lights on in a room that no one was using? A motion sensing light switch allows your light to automatically turn on when someone enters the room. After a preset period of time, if no further motion is sensed the switch automatically turns off the light. In addition to saving energy, motion sensing switches provide "hands - free" switching convenience that's useful in certain situations. Dr. Energy Saver can help you decide which areas of your home can benefit the most from motion sensing controls.

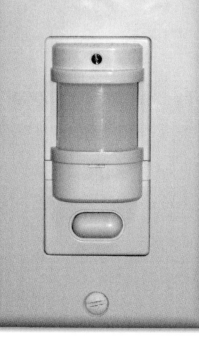

Motion sensor for exterior lighting

Dusk sensor switches improve
convenience and energy savings!

"Did I leave the outdoor lights on all day again?" To eliminate this energy-wasting mistake, Dr. Energy Saver can install dusk sensor controls on some or all of your outdoor lights. This light-sensitive circuitry can be integrated into a light fixture, or available as a retrofit for existing lights. Dr. Energy Saver can help you select which type of dusk-sensing control is best for your house. In either case, once this improvement is made, you never have to worry about turning on outdoor lights every night, or turning them off again in the morning.

Saving **water** *saves* **energy and money**

What does saving water have to do with saving energy? After all, water is a natural resource, like oil or gas, but it's not an energy source. But we use energy, and lots of it, to bring water to our homes and make it work for us. Seeing as you're interested in saving as much energy and money as possible, it's worthwhile to look at ways to use all the water in your home more efficiently. If your home is connected to city water and sewer lines, conserving water will cut your water and sewer bills. If your house has a well and septic system, saving water cuts the costs of pumping water out of the ground into your house. It also helps to avoid overloading your septic system, which can call for expensive pumping. And don't forget about cutting down on hot water use. Since about 15% of your home energy budget goes to heating water, using hot water more efficiently can help cut your utility bills.

Dr. Energy Saver says...

Water is a precious resource we can't afford to waste.

Only 1% of the water on earth is usable for human consumption, and the average home can waste **11,000 gal.** of water a year.

It takes *electricity* to move *water*

As each of us finds ways to use water more efficiently in our homes, we're helping ourselves and our communities. Electricity accounts for 80% of water processing and distribution expenses. On a national level, systems for processing drinking and wastewater consume 50 billion kilowatt-hours annually. That's enough electricity to power more than 4.5 million homes for an entire year. And don't forget where this electricity comes from; burning fossil fuels that are being rapidly depleted. Efficient use and conservation of water saves energy all the way around.

A Shower of Savings ◄ ·······························

The average American uses 140-170 gallons of water per day. A large quantity of that water comes out of a faucet or a showerhead, or is used to flush toilets. Saving water in the shower not only saves the water, (and lightens the load on a septic system if you have one), but more importantly it saves the energy needed to heat the water you didn't use. Eco-friendly shower heads can accomplish this. In faucets, aerators or flow regulators can do the same. Dr. Energy Saver can help you start saving water and energy by evaluating the fixtures in your home and making eco-friendly upgrades as necessary.

www.DrEnergySaver.com

8

Important

Are YOUR appliances Energy Star rated?

8

Water–*saving* appliances

If your clothes washer is not Energy Star rated, it's costing you more than it needs to. Plus, old washing machines aren't just inefficient; they also make clothes wear out faster because of their agitating action. Investing in an Energy Star-rated clothes washer will help save energy dollars while also keeping your wardrobe intact. And remember, if you use hot water to wash your clothes, you'll be saving more than water by upgrading to an eco-friendly model.

Replacing your old dishwasher is also a good way to save on your water and electric bills. A dishwasher made before 1994 typically wastes around 8 gallons per cycle compared to newer models, and costs more to operate. Energy Star-rated dishwashers have innovative features designed to optimize energy and water use, like soil – sensing technology that adjusts the wash cycle based on how dirty your dishes are.

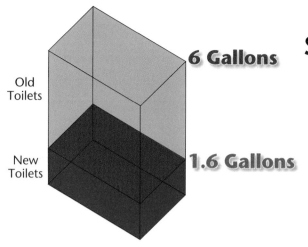

6 Gallons

Old Toilets

New Toilets

1.6 Gallons

Savings from the throne

Saving water is very important in some parts of the country. Besides saving a little money on your city water bill or electricity to operate your well pump, you lighten the load on your septic system or city sewage plant. Today's low flow toilets use 1.6 gallons per flush compared to old toilets at 3-6 gallons per flush. In fact, in the future, you'll likely see toilets with #1 or #2 flush buttons on them. They are available today and save the most.

Eliminating leaks saves *more* than water

The potential for water leaks in a typical house is pretty scary. A leaky faucet can waste over 30 gallons of water a day. A leaking toilet can waste 100 gallons a day. And don't forget the hoses and screw-on connections for your washing machine. While some leaks just waste water (which is bad enough), others can damage floors, walls, carpets, and home furnishings, while encouraging mold to grow wherever moisture lingers.

Dr. Energy Saver can stop leaks that waste water and cost you money. Dr. Energy Saver can also prevent catastrophic leaks by making upgrades in key areas. For example, a FloodRing around your water heater will contain a leak and sound an alarm to tell you there is a problem before damage occurs. You might also want Dr. Energy Saver to replace your standard washing machine supply hoses with heavy-duty FloodChek hoses that are guaranteed not to leak for 20 years. Your washing machine may wear out before these hoses do.

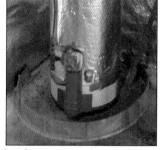

FloodRing around water heater

FloodCheck washing machine hoses will not leak!

Toilet Brick Trick
A little trick to use less water in an older model toilet is to put a brick or full, capped, plastic bottle of water in the toilet tank. That's less water down the drain with each flush - forever!

8

CHAPTER 9 *Windows & Doors*

Can't live *without* 'em

Wanna score some serious energy savings? Just eliminate most of the windows and doors in your house. Yeah, right. Who wants to live in a home that looks and feels like a warehouse? Windows and doors provide views, ventilation and convenient access, while also contributing to the character of your house. These are all significant quality-of-life factors, and after all, isn't that why you love your house? But it's important to make windows and doors as energy efficient as possible, and that's what this chapter is about.

Watch out for the "Big Savings" sales pitch

"The promotion I got in the mail says I can save hundreds of dollars this winter if I get new windows." Boy oh boy, that sure sounds good, and it's "technically" right. It's entirely possible that you might save around $200 ("hundreds" of dollars) per year by replacing old windows with more energy-efficient new windows. But when you consider that the bill to replace all of a home's windows can easily top $15,000, the wisdom of this energy upgrade could be questionable. Saving only a few hundred dollars per year, it would take many years to recover your investment. ***Talk to Dr. Energy Saver before you commit to replacing your windows.*** Consider other energy upgrades with quicker paybacks. Replacing windows makes the most sense when you have very old, excessively leaky windows to start with. Of course, there are aesthetic reasons that may also influence your decision. New windows look and operate better and don't need painting, just so long as you don't get fooled on the big savings sales pitch.

Making windows work *better*

There are a number of ways to make your windows more energy efficient without committing to expensive replacement windows. Dr. Energy Saver can help you decide which upgrades are best for your situation.

▶ Caulk the trim around each window. Sometimes this air-sealing step is all that's required to stop air leakage around each window.

▶ Seal and insulate the shim space. To access the shim space, the window casing (trim) will need to be removed. The same casing can usually be reinstalled after sealing and insulating are done.

▶ Add weatherstripping. If your windows are loose in their jambs or don't close securely, this upgrade can reduce energy loss significantly. Dr. Energy Saver will determine which types of weatherstripping are compatible with your windows, and then properly install the weatherstripping to help make your windows perform better.

▶ Add storm windows. If your existing windows are singlepane windows, you may consider adding storm windows.

"C" Priority

Remember Dr. Energy Saver's ABC Priority for air sealing? Air leaking out of the top of the house is first priority because that's where the highest air pressures are forcing air out. The basement or crawl space is "B" priority because that's where the greatest pressures are sucking air in. The middle of the house is "C" priority because there is the least pressure blowing air out or sucking it in – and that's where your window and doors are. Not that leaky windows, doors or other leaks in the middle are not important – but it makes no sense to do them first and ignore the attic and basement/crawl space.

Dr. Energy Saver says...

Do you feel a cold draft coming in around your windows?

Don't assume that your windows are at fault. Heat moves from hot to cold. Your body may simply feel a chill because it's losing heat to the colder window glass. It's also possible that the shim space between your window frame and your wall framing wasn't properly sealed when the window was installed. Dr. Energy Saver has the equipment and the experience to accurately assess your windows' energy performance.

9

Exterior doors deserve attention

Your doors have to open and close dozens of times a day, and sometimes one side is freezing while the other is a comfortable 70 degrees. Considering what they have to endure, it's not surprising that doors get tired after a while. While your door itself can remain in good shape, it's common for the weatherstripping to gradually deteriorate and stop doing its job. When this happens, the door starts to leak more air, lose energy and cost you money. The good news is that even your old leaky door can be made to seal tightly again when Dr. Energy Saver installs new weatherstripping.

Weatherstripping comes in many shapes and sizes; it's even made from a variety of materials. Foam and V-seal weatherstripping work well around the sides and top of many doors. Along the bottom, a door sweep is often used to seal out the weather. Varying clearances around door edges and other factors mean that the weatherstripping that works for one door won't necessarily work for another. Dr. Energy Saver will know what products will provide the most airtight and durable weather seal for your door.

Dr. Energy Saver says...

Your exterior doors to the outside aren't the only doors that need to have their weatherstripping checked and/or upgraded.

This smart energy-saving upgrade is recommended for any doors to your garage, 3-season porch, or a breezeway.

9

"I need a new entry door. What's the best choice?"

The benefits of installing a new entry door go **beyond** sealing out the weather and improving your home's energy efficiency. Replacing an entry door is a great way to pump up any home's curb appeal. If you're going for this upgrade, look for a door that qualifies as an Energy Star product, and consider the merits and limitations of different door materials as explained below.

Door materials make a difference.

Insulation, weatherstripping and insulated glass are the most important ingredients in an energy-efficient door, but the visible outer surface determines how good a door looks, how long it lasts, and how much it costs.

- **Fiberglass.** This is the door that many people prefer because it's got all the best qualities: strength, durability, energy efficiency and a good variety of style choices. The best-quality fiberglass doors can be made to look remarkably like genuine wood. Beneath the fiberglass exterior skin, there's a core of foam insulation.

- **Solid wood.** The most traditional choice for an exterior door is also the least energy efficient. While it may be historically appropriate for an old house, a solid wood door will swell and shrink with temperature and humidity changes. It can also warp, bow, and crack, making it difficult to maintain a weathertight seal, no matter how carefully weatherstripping is installed.

- **Insulated wood.** This is a good compromise if you want the look of a solid wood door without all of its problems. This type of door has a foam insulation core covered by wood veneer, with narrow solid wood strips along all door edges.

- **Steel.** With a foam core and steel skin, this type of door is solid, stable, durable and energy efficient. Style choices are limited, but you get good value for the money.

- **PVC.** These doors are very similar to fiberglass doors in appearance and construction.

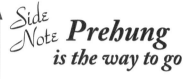

Side Note *Prehung* is the way to go

If you need a new exterior door, it's usually better to install a prehung door than to attempt to fit a new door in an old opening. The term "prehung" means that the door comes already installed in its opening, so the jambs and hinges are already in place. With a quality prehung door, there's no doubt about getting a solid, snug fit in the door jamb, and weatherstripping is already installed. Some prehung doors are actually part of an "entry door system" that can include fixed side windows and transom windows over the door. When buying this type of door, make sure that the windows are insulated (double-pane) glass.

9

"They don't make 'em like they used to."

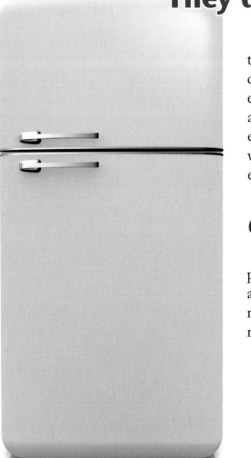

And that's a good thing when it comes to appliances. While it's easy to admire the reliability and retro style of an old refrigerator, you're not doing yourself or the environment any favors by keeping this beast on your energy payroll. Refrigerators are among the biggest energy hogs of all home appliances. A model made before 1990 typically uses about twice as much electricity as a new Energy Star refrigerator. Dollar-wise, the old model will cost you over $100 a year as opposed to around $50 or less for a more-efficient model.

One appliance, TWO prices

When you buy any appliance, there are two costs to consider: the upfront purchase price and the cost of ownership –what you pay to operate the appliance for as long as you own it. If you're operating an old washing machine just because "it still works fine," then you're already paying for a new machine, whether you realize it or not, just by keeping the old one in service.

Dr. Energy Saver says...

Appliances and home electronics account for at least 20% of your total energy bill.

But this percentage can climb even higher depending on how big your family is and what your habits are. Washing a lot of laundry, operating multiple TVs and computers, and using an extra refrigerator or freezer are all factors that can push power use above 20%.

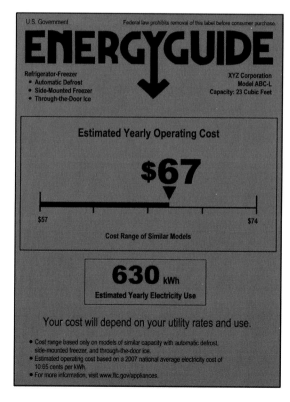

U.S. Government — Federal law prohibits removal of this label before consumer purchase.

ENERGYGUIDE

Refrigerator-Freezer
* Automatic Defrost
* Side-Mounted Freezer
* Through-the-Door Ice

XYZ Corporation
Model ABC-L
Capacity: 23 Cubic Feet

Estimated Yearly Operating Cost

$67

$57 $74

Cost Range of Similar Models

630 kWh
Estimated Yearly Electricity Use

Your cost will depend on your utility rates and use.

* Cost range based only on models of similar capacity with automatic defrost, side-mounted freezer, and through-the-door ice.
* Estimated operating cost based on a 2007 national average electricity cost of 10.65 cents per kWh.
* For more information, visit www.ftc.gov/appliances.

Energy Star helps you shop

The good news is that appliances are much more energy-efficient today than they used to be. Thanks to the Energy Star program, appliance manufacturers are competing to make their products more and more energy efficient. You can take advantage of this when you shop for a new appliance. The information on the yellow Energy Guide label makes it easy to compare different models. You'll see estimates for annual power use, annual operating cost, and a performance range for similar models from other manufacturers. In short, Energy Star makes it easy to buy the most efficient appliances you can afford. But it's still important to read the Energy Guide label. That's because there's quite a range of projected operating costs among Energy Star appliances. For example, a dishwasher must exceed Federal standards by 41% to earn an Energy Star rating. But some Energy Star dishwashers can exceed the Federal standard by over 141%.

10

Saving *more* than electricity

When you upgrade to an Energy Star-rated dishwasher or clothes washer, you'll save water as well as energy. Quite a bit of water, in fact. A dishwasher manufactured before 1994 uses about 8 more gallons of water with every wash cycle, compared to an Energy Star model. An old clothes washer can use 17 more gallons per load than an Energy Star model. And wasting water could mean wasting energy in another way, too, if you're using hot water you paid to heat - a double whammy.

Everyday energy savings

If you've replaced older appliances with Energy Star models, you can amplify your energy savings even further by doing a few simple things:

- Don't neglect proper maintenance. Dr. Energy Saver can make sure your appliances are operating at peak efficiency by performing basic maintenance and verifying that appliance settings are correct.

- Only wash full loads in the dishwasher.

- Eliminate the dishwasher's powered drying cycle and allow dishes to air-dry.

- Only wash full loads of clothes, and use cold water for wash and rinse cycles whenever possible.

- Make sure to keep the lint filter clean in your clothes dryer. Have Dr. Energy Saver upgrade your flexible "white hose" to a solid metal vent, so your drier can circulate more air and dry your clothes faster.

www.DrEnergySaver.com

10

WHEN "OFF" = "ON"

Ever heard of "phantom loads?" That's what happens when you turn off your computers, printers, television monitors and other devices, but instead of being off, they are actually in "sleep" or "standby" mode. We think the power is "off," but it's really not. Added together, the phantom electrical loads in a house can account for up to a staggering 5% of your electric bill. Some phantom loads (like the digital clock on your kitchen range, for example) aren't worth turning off. Many others are. To cut down on phantom loads, you can plug associated devices (computer, printer, phone recharger) into a single power strip so that everything can be turned off at once by turning off the strip. Dr. Energy Saver can also help by providing you with "Smart Strips" that are designed to automatically turn off several devices when just a single "main" device is turned off. For example, these intelligent strips can turn off your DVD player, surround sound system, and converter box when you turn off your television. This saves you money that is normally wasted *when "off" = "on."*

!
Important

10

CHAPTER 11 *Renewable Energy*

From CONSERVATION *To* GENERATION—

The first 10 chapters in this book are devoted to helping you conserve energy. If you've looked through any of these chapters, you know that there are quite a few ways to improve energy efficiency and squeeze as much value as possible from a home energy budget.

In this chapter, we move from conservation to generation – utilizing renewable energy sources to generate energy and achieve even greater savings. Renewable energy has great green value because it's clean and inexhaustible. We're never going to run out of sun or wind. But harnessing these green resources costs money. If you're interested in tapping into renewable resources, make sure you tap into Dr. Energy Saver's expertise in this area, too.

From a financial point of view, conservation is much more important than investing in alternative energy sources that generate more expensive energy. In other words, you wouldn't make a big investment, generate expensive energy, and then waste it on an inefficient house. As the years click by and technologies advance and prices come down, the decision factors on renewable energy sources will change.

Dr. Energy Saver will either be able to provide you with such installations, or work closely with a specialist who does.

You'll Love This!

The energy-saving improvements in this chapter may qualify for Federal and/or state rebates, which makes them even more attractive. Dr. Energy Saver can help you determine what incentives may apply to any upgrades you're considering.

Geothermal systems ROCK!

If you've read Chapter 5, you already know about heat pumps. In the summer, a heat pump functions as an air conditioner, moving heat from inside your house to the outside. During the winter, this cycle is reversed, allowing the heat pump to warm your living space. Geothermal heat pumps (a.k.a ground-source heat pumps) represent sustainable "green" technology because they're much more efficient than other HVAC systems and because they utilize a renewable resource: the earth's ability to store and release heat.

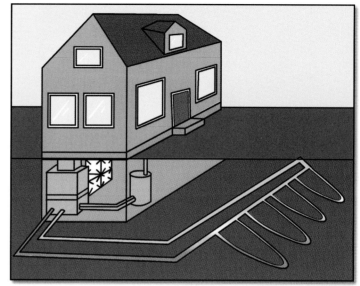

As shown in the drawing, a geothermal heat pump utilizes tubing buried in the ground to either dump heat from the house to the ground (cooling mode) or transfer heat from the ground to the house (heating mode). The steady year-round temperature of the earth (55-65 degrees below the frost line) is what makes geothermal heat pumps so efficient. As a bonus, many of these systems can also take care of heating your water, so in certain instances, there may be no need for a separate water heater.

The only potential down side to a geothermal heat pump is the upfront investment and disruption to your yard. Trenches or deep holes need to be made to bury the tubing loops deep enough to harness the earth's temperature. Technological advances are being made that may soon bring down costs and provide options that are significantly less disruptive to your yard. Dr. Energy Saver can help determine if this excellent renewable option makes sense for your home.

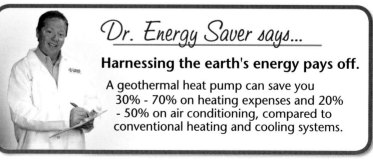

Dr. Energy Saver says...

Harnessing the earth's energy pays off.

A geothermal heat pump can save you 30% - 70% on heating expenses and 20% - 50% on air conditioning, compared to conventional heating and cooling systems.

11

81

A water heater on your roof

Solar water heating systems, also known as "Solar Thermal" systems, have been in use for many years, and it's easy to understand why. In sunny climates, a solar hot water system can cut water-heating expenses by as much as 80%. Savings will be less in areas where sunshine is less reliable, but even a 50% reduction in colder climates can amount to hundreds of dollars saved per year. **In addition to cutting your water heating costs, solar thermal can sometimes be integrated with your home's heating system to provide significant savings there, too.** If your house provides good opportunities for solar thermal, Dr. Energy Saver will explain the best system options as well as possible financial incentives to help offset initial system installation costs.

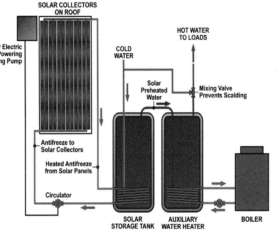

How solar thermal systems work

A collector captures the sun's heat to warm water or an antifreeze solution that is pumped down to a tank-type water heater when it reaches a predetermined temperature. The water heater only comes on if solar-heated water needs additional warming.

You'll Love This!

Dr. Energy Saver says...

Make sure you're conserving energy before you start generating energy.

Solar power and wind energy get plenty of publicity these days, but it's important to put these high-profile technologies in perspective when deciding how to improve your home's energy performance. It's much smarter to complete higher return on investment, less-expensive energy upgrades like air sealing, additional insulation, duct sealing, and equipment upgrades before you think about solar PV and wind power. These other common sense energy-saving upgrades pay for themselves much faster.

11

Solar electricity is expensive

Photovoltaic (PV) technology has come a long way since the early days of our space program, when satellites were powered by primitive PV arrays that turned sunlight into electricity. Today, PV performance has improved and there are even photovoltaic roof shingles that can make a PV installation almost invisible. But PV power is still very expensive. It's not very efficient either, since electricity is consumed converting the direct current (DC) that comes from the PV array into alternating current (AC) for household use. With PV, you're paying a lot just to gain a little. That's why solar thermal is a much smarter investment. Solar PV can be part of your overall strategy to save money, but it is way down the list in terms of investment priorities.

What about the wind?

Wind power is similar to PV power in terms of performance and cost, plus the added challenge of neighborhood and zoning issues. The potential to harness this renewable resource is limited. Only about half of the land mass in the U.S. has enough wind to power small wind turbines. If you're interested in this green technology, Dr. Energy Saver can recommend a wind contractor in your area.

Heating with wood and pellets works - if <u>you</u> do

A wide range of stoves and furnaces are available for burning wood and pellets. People rely on these fuels to reduce their use of fuel oil or gas. But unlike solar and wind power, heating with wood or pellets isn't always clean and it demands a certain amount of work on the part of the homeowner.

For wood or pellet heat to be safe, sustainable and cost-effective, you need to be using an EPA-certified stove or furnace that has been professionally installed. Safe, efficient operation depends on the use of dry, high-quality fuel. If you plan to use a woodstove or pellet stove on a regular basis, have Dr. Energy Saver make sure that this heat source doesn't compromise the safe, efficient operation of your HVAC system.

11

What do I do now?

If you haven't already, call your local Dr. Energy Saver at their local number. If you don't know it, call 1-877-4RX-ENERGY (1-877-479-3637) and we'll direct you to the right "Doctor" in your area.

The Doctor and a team member will come out to do a complete energy check-up and give you our Home Energy Report Card™. We'll prioritize what repairs should be made first, second, third, etc., and tell you exactly what it will cost to fix. Then you decide what repairs you want to go ahead with so you can begin saving energy and money right away!

How much you save will depend on what improvements you decide to invest in, how inefficient your current situation is, and of course comparative energy prices and weather. Energy upgrades are smart investments because they pay for themselves - you're going to pay whether you get them or not!

Thank you for your attention to this important subject. We look forward to serving you today!

Your Prescription for Lower Energy Bills™

www.DrEnergySaver.com

About the Authors

Tim Snyder is a publishing and communications specialist with expertise in green living, home improvement and building technology. Tim has written books on house construction, deck building and furniture making. He coauthored two "New Yankee Workshop" books with Norm Abram, and has worked as the editor of Fine Homebuilding and American Woodworker magazines. Tim's magazine articles have been featured in This Old House, Time, and Men's Health. His last project before joining the Dr. Energy Saver team was a "Green Remodeling Guide" for historic houses in northern California.

The energy Tim uses outside of Dr. Energy Saver is spread out among a few favorite activities that include tennis, woodworking, home improvement and hanging out with an amazing wife (Barbara), two exceptional children (Sarah and Ian), and a yellow lab (Brawley) who loves to hide socks.

Tom Casey is a third generation comfort and energy conservation specialist. His grandfather, John Casey, started in the early 1900s delivering coal and ice. His father, Tom Casey Sr., continued the family tradition, evolving into the fuel oil delivery and HVAC industries. Tom got involved as a youth and developed a passion for the business.

Tom is a nationally recognized expert in comfort and energy conservation for homes and commercial buildings. He is a frequent contributor to various national trade publications including Contracting Business Magazine, as well as being a speaker at industry conferences. His companies have won 10 national awards and in 2001 he was awarded the prestigious National Residential Contractor of the Year award.

Tom was born and raised in Milford, CT, and continues to reside there today with his wife Dana, and three children: Abigayle, Deklin, and Jenna. He enjoys motorcycling, skiing, and spending time with his family. Tom is involved in the community serving various charities, plus he is very active on a state level with consumer protection and energy conservation advocacy issues.   Web resources – *Click4Climate.com*

About the Authors

Larry Janesky became a self-employed carpenter at age 17, and built his first home at age 18. He was a builder and general contractor for five years, building 23 homes. In 1987, Larry started Basement Systems, soon becoming the largest radon mitigation contractor in the country, and then the largest basement waterproofing contractor as well. He recruited other waterproofing contractors to join the Basement Systems network, and has personally trained thousands of people from 6 countries on basement waterproofing, radon, crawl space repair, basement finishing, and energy conservation. Larry has 25 patents. In addition, Larry is a specialist in contractor business management, and is a sought-after speaker. He publishes a daily blog at thinkdaily.com, and has written 6 books. His latest is entitled "The Highest Calling – an inspirational novel about business and life, struggle and success" and is available at *TheHighestCallingBook.com*.

Larry is native of Bridgeport, Connecticut. He lives in Middlebury, CT, with his wife Wendy, and their three children: Tanner, Chloe and Autumn. He is an avid motocross racer, and enjoys the outdoors. Larry chooses to make the world a better place not only through energy conservation and quality home improvement services, but through contractor business training to benefit customers, employees, and businesses.

Web resources – *DrEnergySaver.com*, *BasementSystems.com*, *TotalBasementFinishing.com*, *FoundationSupportworks.com*, *LarryJanesky.com*.

Notes

Notes

_____

_____

_____

_____

_____

_____

_____

_____

_____

_____

Dr. ENERGY saver™

Your Prescription for Lower Energy Bills™

www.DrEnergySaver.com